D0393744

TALES FROM SEVEN GHETTOS

TALES FROM SEVEN GHETTOS

By
EGON ERWIN KISCH

Translated into English by Edith Bone

ROBERT ANSCOMBE & CO. LTD.
LONDON

First Edition 1948

PRINTED BY THE ALCUIN PRESS, WELWYN GARDEN CITY, FOR THE PUBLISHER
ROBERT ANSCOMBE & CO., LTD., 291/293 GRAYS INN ROAD, LONDON, W.C.I.

CONTENTS

CHAPTER ONE

The Taming of Scabhead

COULD I tell you the real story of what happened to Councillor Samek of the corn exchange and why he suddenly turned up in your house and in the houses of your neighbours? Could I tell you? Of course I could, but would it interest these other people who don't even know who Councillor Samek the grain-broker is, much less. . . ? What's that? You all know his name, because he is so well known? All right, but have you ever heard of Mendel Mandel?

Of course you have never heard of him, those of you who are not natives of Grosmeserich. I'm not surprised that you describe Councillor Samek as a famous man, nor that you have never heard of Mendel Mandel.

For Councillor Samek is the richest man among the "Moravians"—which is what the Bohemian Jews call their Moravian co-religionists. He is the sole owner of the mill in Grosmeserich that goes under the name of Bergman, Neugröschl, Pacovski & Co., having ousted all Bergmanns, Neugröschls, Pacovskis and the whole Company from the mill. It is now his alone and the grain market in Vienna dances to his tune.

Mendel Mandel on the other hand—Mendel Mandel is not prominent at all. You would know him only if you came from the Grosmeserich district and in that case you would certainly not ask why Mendel Mandel turned up in your houses and in those of your neighbours, as you asked why Councillor Samek the grain-broker came to your houses and those of your neighbours that time.

For if you came from Grosmeserich you would know that Mendel Mandel comes to every house punctually at his set hour and that not many residents of the district of Grosmeserich, inasmuch as they belong to the Mosaic faith, can boast of having got Mendel Mandel to leave their houses with empty hands.

For Mendel Mandel the *schnorrer* is just as efficient in his way as Samek the grain-broker is in his and therefore poor Mendel Mandel is by no means as poor as rich Councillor Samek is rich. True that even were he as poor as Councillor Samek is rich, he would still be unknown, because poverty never makes a man famous. In order to be famous, one must be rich or achieve something unusual or invent something, even if it is only some fruitless thing, like the invention of that Onan whose name is still known after so many thousand years.

But now it is time for me to enlighten you as to how it happened that Samek the grain-broker turned up in your houses on a certain occasion and what it all had to do with Mendel Mandel.

Mendel Mandel's son had studied law in Vienna, then taken his degree and was working there in a lawyer's office. Miss Ellen Samek was also living in Vienna. She had gone there to attend the young ladies' school run by a Mrs. Schwarzwald, as befitted the adolescent daughter of a good Jewish family. At the school she devoted herself to physical jerks and sports, as especially befitted an adolescent daughter of a good Jewish family who was very, very stout. She weighed a goodish bit over fourteen stone and that was decidedly too much even for the adolescent daughter of a good Jewish family. It is quite easy to understand that a millionaire does not allow his only child to grow sour in Grosmeserich but sends his daughter to the big city in order that she may reduce her weight properly and bring home a suitable son-in-law to Papa; but I am afraid that what I am going to add now will appear quite incredible to some of you and at the same time lay me open to a charge of stark banality. But there is nothing for it, I must tell you for all that:

Alphonse Mandel, LL.D. and Miss Ellen Samek met in Vienna and fell in love.

I know perfectly well that at this point you will shout: "Stop! What, in Vienna, a city of several million inhabitants—these two people from Grosmeserich are supposed to have met each other? Why didn't you bring them together in Grosmeserich? Must you drag in Vienna to get on with your story?"

No, I don't need Vienna for my story at all; however many are the places to which it will take us, as you shall soon hear, all these places without exception are in the district of Grosmeserich, while Vienna is in quite another part of the country.

Besides, my story isn't my story at all, it is the story of Ellen Samek and of Alphonse Mandel, LL.D. and of their respective fathers; and that the two young people met in Vienna instead of Grosmeserich is a fact which I cannot change.

But—and here I pass from the defensive to the offensive—the fact that Ellen and Alphonse did meet in Vienna is not only an accidental truth, it is also the only possible truth. Where else could they have met? In Grosmeserich perhaps? Don't make me laugh! In that narrow space an abyss of astronomical proportions gapes between the daughter of the richest member and President of the Jewish community and the son of a poor man, the local *schnorrer!* She would never catch so much as a glimpse of him or he of her.

In Vienna, on the contrary, this was not only possible, it was quite a matter of course. If you come from Grosmeserich, you have a lot of friends with whom you were at school together at Trebitch—such former schoolfellows in turn have married girls from Boscovits or Goding, who again have cousins who—in short it would have been the devil's own work if Ellen Samek and Alphonse Mandel, LL.D. had not chanced on each other in Vienna. And since up to that point the devil had had nothing to do with it, Ellen and Alphonse did chance on each other and got engaged.

Samek the grain-broker knew nothing of it all. Ellen dared not tell him of her engagement. As for Mendel Mandel, he too was kept in the dark for a long time. He could have had no objection to the matter in itself. Ellen was a splendid match for his son, although he never spoke of Samek the grain-broker without calling him contemptuously "that scabhead". Now a scabhead is by no means a person whose head is covered with scabs; it is applied to a man who does not raise his hat when he returns a greeting, as though he had a scab to conceal. In actual fact such a man has no scab to conceal, he is only conceited, a scabhead.

Young Mr. Mandel in Vienna knew that his father called his fiancée's father a scabhead, but that was certainly no reason why they should fear that Mendel Mandel would not give his consent to the marriage. Mendel Mandel being the lesser evil for the engaged couple, it was he who was let into the secret first and it was he undertook to break the news to the other future father-in-law.

One day Mendel Mandel, on entering the office of Bergmann, Neugröschl, Pacovski & Co., where he received his weekly hand-out from usually one of the book-keepers, demanded to see the head of the firm himself. (Of course he did not say "that scabhead" but Councillor Samek.) For this time it was not a matter of *schnorren*—he had a very important communication to make to Councillor Samek.

When Samek the grain-broker heard the communication, which was indeed of the greatest importance to him, he turned as red as a lobster, measured Mendel Mandel with a mixture of fury and disgust and threw him out.

"Threw him out". That's soon said. One can call it "throwing someone out" if for instance one gives him no answer to a question; one can "throw someone out" by simply getting up and thereby indicating that the interview is at an end; one "throws out" by showing the visitor the door; one "throws out" by shouting, "Get out!"

But Samek the grain-broker did not use any of these methods to throw out Mendel Mandel. He actually did *throw* him out. He, the scabhead, who otherwise would never soil his hands by touching a *schnorrer*, he grabbed little Mendel Mandel by both shoulders, flung him against the door, tore the door wide open, and spat into Mendel Mandel's face. "Schnorrer!" he roared. "Schnorrer!" he spat and shoved and kicked Mendel Mandel to the stairs, so that Mendel Mandel tumbled down them head over heels and it was a miracle that he did not break both his legs.

Not satisfied with having pushed his visitor down the stairs, Samek the grain-broker tore open the window and while Mendel Mandel, groaning and trembling, was feeling his limbs for possible fractures and wiping the spittle from his face in the yard, he ordered the gatekeeper to "take this *schnorrer* by the scruff of the neck and throw him out of the yard" and also to release the dog from the chain if this *schnorrer*, this *schnorrer*, ever dared to show his face in the factory again. (Samek never called his mill anything but "factory".)

Mendel Mandel was outside the factory. He clenched his fists and hissed "Scabhead!", but Samek the grain-broker did not hear him, for he had already slammed the window shut. As for the employees who looked inquisitively out of other windows, the word "scabhead" was nothing new to them, for it was what they themselves called their employer behind his back.

News of the incident was immediately relayed to Vienna to its two authors who thus learned what had befallen that day in Grosmeserich between their own two authors, their fathers.

Mendel Mandel conveyed the news in a letter. Writing was not his strong suit (there are *writing-schnorrers* too, but he was not one of them) and as he described the result of his intervention to his son, the memory of the occurrence excited him to such an extent that the letters staggered and tumbled over one another as he wrote them down.

Yes, Mendel Mandel was greatly incensed. Why? Because he had been thrown out? Not at all. The profession of a *schnorrer*, like that of a boxer, demands the ability to take it. When I say "take it" I don't of course mean the taking of gifts; no, "taking it" in the *schnorrer's* trade means putting up with insults and humiliations including that of being thrown out. Mendel Mandel possessed this ability; in his long life he had had every opportunity of acquiring and testing it.

What had roused him to fury was not just that he had been thrown out once more that day. Possibly—there is no clue to it in the letter and so I put forward this suggestion merely as a surmise—possibly his feelings were hurt because he had been spat upon and thrown out not in his quality of *schnorrer*, but as a private visitor, as a suitor on behalf of his son the LL.D., an LL.D. with two degrees, an LL.D. of Vienna University.

There was also another point. Some indications of this may be found both in the letter written by Mendel Mandel to his son and in his subsequent behaviour. He felt insulted because his profession had been insulted, a profession which he had followed all his life and which had enabled him to give his son a good education and make him into an LL.D., an LL.D. with two degrees, an LL.D. of Vienna University! It may sound an exaggeration but it is fact: had Samek, "that scabhead", called him a rogue, a blackmailer, a highway robber, yea, even if he had called him a *filthy* schnorrer, a *miserable* schnorrer, instead of calling him just a *schnorrer* again and again, Mendel Mandel would have resented it far less.

This was why Mendel Mandel, in his letter, decried the methods with which Samek had made his money. "I could have done the same," wrote Mendel Mandel. "I could do the same even now, I could drive once every week to the corn exchange and swindle the public! I could drive about in a motor-car," wrote Mendel Mandel, and he was quite right, "I too could drive about in a motor-car, if I had one. But I haven't got one," wrote Mendel Mandel "so I must climb up and down a lot of stairs to earn my bread" and in this he was right again, although a motor-car would not have been much use to him in climbing a lot of stairs. "And then such a scabhead comes along" wrote Mendel Mandel and in this he was wrong, for it had not been the scabhead who had *come* along, but Mendel Mandel who had *gone* along—but we have no wish to analyse the statements contained in the letter and the psychological motives of the writer's excitement; all we want to do is to relate briefly and to the point what was actually written in the letter.

What was actually in the letter was chiefly a curse on Samek the scabhead unto the second and third generation. Understand this: such a curse meant that if his Alphonse were to marry Samek's daughter, he would not only marry a woman accursed, he would also beget children with a curse on them. Not content with that, Mendel Mandel urged his son to beget such an in advance anathematized progeny, but an illegitimate one. "Give her a baby and then leave her to nurse her big belly"—thus in his furious thirst for revenge he commanded his son.

Even more irrevocable than the curse laid on three

generations was the announcement Mendel Mandel made in his letter, that he would that very day go to a lawyer and sue Samek for assault "and if I have to spend my last penny, I will not rest until that scabhead appears before a criminal court and all the newspapers write about him."

While Mendel Mandel was snorting over this letter, Samek the grain-broker raced to Vienna in his car. He burst into his daughter's room, said, "Pack your things!" and asked no questions. Since she asked none either, everything was quite clear.

Father, daughter and luggage drove back home together. The distance between Vienna and Grosmeserich is one hundred and twenty miles and for one hundred and twenty miles not a word was spoken.

The next few weeks were an unhappy time. Mendel Mandel spent most of it in his lawyer's office and Ellen Samek visibly lost weight. "Visibly" is not the right word though. "Ominously" would be better. What no slimming cure, dieting and gymnastics had ever accomplished, she was now losing weight so fast that Samek the grain-broker, who had at first observed this effect of being crossed in love with a certain amount of secret satisfaction, now began to be seriously worried.

The doctor was called in but did nothing to allay these anxieties; on the contrary he found the loss of weight abnormal and ordered a fattening cure. In spite of this and in contradiction of the saying that time cured all ills, Ellen's condition grew steadily worse and her net weight of fourteen stone had dropped to ten stone two pounds four ounces. (By now Ellen was being weighed to limits of one-thirtieth of an ounce.)

What could Samek the grain-broker do? He did not want his only child to die of a slow consumption, so there was nothing left for him to do but to drive to Vienna and give Ellen's betrothed his paternal consent with a generous

gesture. Alphonse Mandel of course, expressed his satisfaction at this, but it was a painful sort of satisfaction. For
Alphonse Mandel, LL.D., declared that it was impossible
for him to go against the wishes of an old father who had
for a lifetime deprived himself of every penny for the sake
of his son. He could not offend his father, was afraid his
father would prove obdurate and was certain that even if
the marriage took place, Mendel Mandel would not withdraw from the lawsuit or be deterred by any scandal.

With great fervour but without much hope, young
Mandel promised to see his father again, but made it perfectly clear that he would not dare to marry without his
father's consent.

Mendel Mandel remained inexorable, and let his son
Alphonse, LL.D., with two degrees, go back to Vienna
with nothing achieved. Ellen tipped the scales at 112 lbs.
7 ozs. Grain-broker Samek, the scabhead, had no choice
but to go and see Mendel Mandel. Mendel Mandel gave
full vent to his feelings but Samek the grain-broker listened
to the ravings of the district *schnorrer* with the meekness of a
Hillel.

"Very good. And what are your conditions, Mr.
Mandel?"

"My conditions?" cried Mendel Mandel and a triumphant gleam in his eye betrayed to what extent he had
longed to hear that very question ever since his eviction
from the factory and how carefully he had prepared to
answer it. "You want to know my conditions?"

"Yes."

"I have only one condition. Do you want to hear it?"

"Yes."

"My condition is that you go out *schnorring* for one whole
day, as I have had to do for forty years, from eight in the
morning to six in the evening. If you go *schnorring* between
Grosmeserich and Golchyenikow for one whole day, from

eight in the morning until six in the evening, your daughter can have my son the doctor of law, but not otherwise; that I swear by the life of my Alphonse."

It was too much. Councillor Samek, the grain-broker, for all that he had been resolved to accept any condition, turned on his heel and stalked out.

Not until Ellen's weight had dropped to 98 lbs. 3 ozs. did he go to see Mendel Mandel again and declare that he accepted the condition.

So the next day Samek the grain-broker went on that round the meaning of which you wanted to know. You are not the first to ask the same question: the inhabitants of the district of Grosmeserich were still putting forward plenty of surmises regarding this expedition of Samek the grain-broker even at the time when the world war was already offering quite enough other subjects for gossip. Punctually at eight o'clock that morning Councillor Samek, of the corn exchange, reported for duty. Mendel Mandel accompanied him to see that he did not shirk, and pointed out the Jewish houses the new *schnorrer* was now to "make".

Like a pimp watching whether his woman does not slack on the job, did Mendel Mandel ever lie in wait at the nearest corner to see that the scabhead did not dodge a single house. Willy-nilly, Samek the grain-broker had to go in. The master of the house received him with obsequious apologies about the state of the house which had not yet been cleaned and tidied at such an early hour, but Samek, more obsequiously still, interrupted such apologies with the announcement that he had come to *schnorr*. At first the master of the house would not understand: he would smile and think it was a joke. But Samek the *schnorrer* would begin—as per instructions of Mendel Mandel—to pour out, in passionate tones, an entirely untrue tale of woe. The mill had gone bankrupt, everything had been seized, and there was not a crust of bread left for himself and—here Samek had to shed tears—for his daughter. Any little gift would be welcome: "Please give me a few pence, God will reward you for it."

Oh yes? Was that so? Now the fun would begin. Questions and taunts would rain down on the grain-broker who would have liked to sink into the ground, had that not been contrary to the agreement with Mendel Mandel.

"Oh, so that's it? So you are a *schnorrer* at last? Would you have given me something perhaps, if I had come to you to *schnorr* when you were rich? You would not even have allowed me inside the house! Didn't you put up my community contribution because my wife gets her clothes made by a dressmaker in Brno? 'Let your wife have her clothes made here in Grosmeserich'—that was what you said when I complained of the increased tax. Not a penny will I give you, as true as I live!"

In every house the novice *schnorrer* visited, he heard different reproaches, but the burden was always the same: "Not a penny will I give you, as true as I live!" "Every spring I advance the peasants money so they can till their fields, and let myself in for a lot of headaches whether I'll ever see my money again.—But in summer—of course only if grain prices are high—along comes Councillor Samek, of the corn exchange, with his well-pressed trousers, gives the peasants money so they can pay me back my advance and then Councillor Samek buys the crop himself. No, not a penny will I give you, as true as I live!"

Thus did they swear, but if they themselves did not combine their pledge with a dive into their pocket and did not throw the hated Samek a coin, it was the wife who would do so, on the one hand because the wives did not want their husbands to perjure themselves and on the other hand because they thought an impoverished manu-

B

facturer far more deserving of sympathy than a born *schnorrer*. That was probably how Samek fared in your houses and those of your neighbours when he called on you so unexpectedly.

Little by little Samek grew less and less sensitive. He was no longer pained when he was abused by the person from whom he *schnorrered*. Nevertheless he blanched when, in Yeshovits, he came face to face with Max Pacovski. Max Pacovski was a brother of one of the former partners in "Bergman, Neugröschl, Pacovski & Co." For almost thirty years he had worked in the mill, ten years of the thirty after his brother had already been driven out of the firm and Samek the grain-broker had become the sole owner. Then one day Samek had dismissed Max Pacovski without notice and without valid reason, in order to give his job to someone with good connections.

Max Pacovski said: "I despise you because you are a vile exploiter. Years ago I would have gladly sacrificed my last penny in order to sue you, but I knew that a rich man is never hurt by being sued."

"Now I am a poor man, Mr. Pacovski. Please give me a few coppers, God will reward you for it."

"I will not give you a bent farthing. But I will lend you ten crowns at 10 per cent. Here's the money, write me a receipt."

"I can't borrow any money, Mr. Pacovski, I could never pay you back. So give me something as a gift, I am a *schnorrer*."

"You're no *schnorrer*, Samek. A rich man never gets to be a *schnorrer* in this world; crooks don't let each other down and it's the crooks that have the money. Only when one day the money is taken away from all the crooks at the same time, will you be a *schnorrer*."

In other circumstances Samek the grain-broker would have made plenty of trouble for Max Pacovski because of this subversive talk, but as a *schnorrer* he could say nothing; as a *schnorrer* he could only take the money and sign the receipt and even that was actually rather more than he should have done as a *schnorrer*.

When a village was "done", Samek the grain-broker met Mendel Mandel on the outskirts and they walked to-gether to the next village. Mandel was curious to know how much Samek had been given in this house and that; more than once he shook his head in acknowledgment of Samek's performance:

"More than I can earn there!"

"How much do you usually take on the stretch we have just done, Mr. Mandel?"

"In Brennporitschen I make about three crowns, in Budwitz four-fifty, in Baritsch two, in Cheboshitz another two—altogether about eleven crowns. And how much have you made?"

Samek the grain-broker struck a balance: he had got twenty-four crowns and seventy hellers, but of course ten crowns were only a loan, the money from Max Pacovski.

They went on. The roads between one Moravian village and another are bad, particularly in the district of Gros-meserich. Samek had to rest quite often, but Mendel Mandel waited obligingly. All he did was to ask sar-castically: "Driving in a motor-car is better, isn't it?"

The morning went by, the hot midday, the first hours of the afternoon. They had left the village of Libshits behind and twenty-seven crowns and thirty hellers of shamefully scrounged money jingled in Councillor Samek's pocket, but Goltch-Yenokow was near at hand, it lacked only an hour to six o'clock and then the ordeal would be over.

They climbed the hill from Libshits to Goltch-Yenikow. It was further than they had thought, the road was steeper than they had thought and their legs had grown weary.

Finally Samek and Mandel saw Goltch-Yenikow lying at their feet; it was a town inhabited by prosperous and charitable Jews. The clock in the church tower struck half-past five, the cornfields swayed in the evening breeze and there was a scent in the air of white, plaited Sabbath bread.

Mendel Mandel halted and drew a deep breath. "Mechutan", he said (Mechutan is the word a father uses to address the father-in-law of his own child) "Mechutan" he said and held out his right hand towards the man who had humiliated him and whom he had humiliated this day. In a voice quivering with emotion he added: "Now we will go home and our children will get married and be happy."

Samek the grain-broker seized the proffered hand and shook it. Then he took his watch out of his pocket, considered for a little while and then suggested:

"We really still have time to do Goltsch-Yenikow, you know!"

CHAPTER TWO

Danton's Death and Popper's Nephew

IN THE cemetery in the Rue des Errancis near the Monceau barrier the headless corpses of the brothers Frey of Brno fell to dust in the same grave with the headless corpses of Danton and Camille Desmoulins. The two brothers Frey embraced fraternally before they offered themselves to the falling knife.

When on the sixteenth of Germinal in the year II. (5th April, 1794) the tumbril carried them to the place of execution, Danton and Desmoulins heard no cries of friendship or sympathy; what fell on their ear was the old doggerel, sung tauntingly for the benefit of Chabot and Basire, their colleagues in the Convention and now riding with them in the tumbril:

> Connaiît-on jamais rien de pire
> Que Chabot, Merlin et Basire
> Et jamais rien de plus sot
> Que Basire, Merlin et Chabot

The brothers Frey were not even deemed worthy of a jeer. Only fragments of the inarticulate noise that accompanied the tumbrils from the Conciergerie to the Place de la Révolution may have referred to the two financier-speculators who had corrupted members of the Convention and pushed the Revolution and the Republic to the brink of the abyss.

It was not his imprisonment, not the tribunal and not the certainty of the scaffold that had roused Danton to a burst of fury in the courtroom—what had driven Danton to frenzy was that his case had been linked with that of Deputy Chabot who had sold himself for a pretty bride

and hard cash. For a Danton to have to sit in the same
dock with a Chabot and his accomplices, with stock-
jobbers and share-pushers, to have to ride through all
Paris with the two bankers Frey and mingle his gushing
blood with that of the speculators!

"Siegman Gottlob Junius Frey, thirty-six years old,
born at Brno, Moravia, domiciled in Paris, Rue d'Anjou,
Faubourg St. Honoré,

Emanuel Frey, twenty-six years old, born in Brno in
Moravia, domiciled Rue d'Anjou, brother of the above
and like he, brother-in-law to Chabot,

are accused as initiators, aiders and abettors of a conspiracy to corrupt certain members of the Convention and
thereby offending against the dignity of the people's representation and attempting to undermine the Convention."

Thus is it set down in the act of accusation put forward
by Fouquier-Tinville on the 9th of Germinal, Year II.

"The brothers Frey," says the public prosecutor, "foreign
ex-aristocrats, ex-barons, are agents of England and of the
Vienna cabinet, although they assumed the mask of
revolutionary patriotism. Their brother-in-law Chabot
stated that they had been hanged in effigy in Vienna and
their estates confiscated—he said this in order to make us
believe in their love of freedom. But although their pro-
perty is supposed to have been confiscated, they have
found the means of giving their sister a dowry of 200,000
livres and thereby inducing Chabot to marry a foreign
woman of aristocratic extraction. Never had corruption-
ists spread their nets with greater audacity and ruthless-
ness, never had conspirators uncovered more shamelessly
the true objectives of their machinations. The Danish
court advocate Deiderichsen (Diederichs), who formerly
lived in Vienna and came to France in 1792, is an agent
of the Frey brothers and serves them in their speculations;
his whole attitude stamps him as nothing but the tool of

their plottings. Although he claims to have lived only on
the bounty of the said brothers Frey, he was able to lend
private persons considerable sums of money, to live a life
of luxury, and put through important commercial deals
abroad. Finally, at the moment when he recognized that
the chain binding together all these machinations was
damaged or even broken, he attempted to leave French
territory with certain sums of money allegedly entrusted
to him by the said brothers Frey."

The brothers Frey had planned nothing less than to
induce the national assembly to pass a fictitious decision
dissolving the Compagnie des Indes, the most prosperous
French importing company. The brothers Frey wanted
to buy up the shares thus rendered valueless, and then sell
them at a good price after the official publication of the
Convention decision. For there was to be an addendum
to the decision, granting the council of administration of
the company the right to liquidate the company and in
the interim to wind up its current business.

It was on the 17th of Vendémiaire (8th October, 1793)
that Delaunay, bribed by the Freys, made his speech
against the Compagnie des Indes; the clarion call with
which he blared forth his motion for dissolution, his
description of the tax frauds, of the corruption, of the
methods by which the council of administration transformed taxable assets into liabilities, was loud and shrill.
All the softer was the chamade of the addendum which was
intended to be drowned by the outbursts of indignation.

But the Convention was nothing less than a voting
machine; the courage which enabled the members of that
assembly to face the machinations of the monarchists and
reactionaries without trembling was combined with a very
sensitive ear for the tricks of those who sought to turn the
revolution to their personal advantage. Scarcely had
Delaunay ended when Fabre d'Églantine mounted the

rostrum: "After the attacks made by the reporting member," said this playwright who might have been expected to show himself more at home in matters relating to the arts than to finance, "after these ponderous accusations against the Compagnie des Indes, I must express my surprise that he has not moved its immediate complete dissolution. It is impossible to proceed too severely against men who have cheated the nation of fifty million livres. Therefore I move that the government confiscate without delay all the goods of the Compagnie and cause them to be sold by the organs of the state. Further let all the books be sealed in order to safeguard the proofs of the frauds perpetrated by the members of the council of administration."

Robespierre also opposed the member reporting and supported the motion of Fabre d'Églantine. Amendments are proposed and the matter referred to a committee of five consisting of Fabre d'Églantine, Ramel, Cambon and the two bribed men Delaunay and Chabot.

The racketeers must therefore corrupt one more member of the committee in order to obtain a majority. That is not as easy as the brothers Frey imagine. They give Chabot 100,000 francs with which to bribe Fabre d'Églantine. But when Chabot submits the draft decree to Fabre d'Églantine in the ante-chamber of the assembly and asks him to sign it, Fabre reads it carefully, immediately deletes the sentence providing for the Compagnie des Indes to liquidate its own affairs—the sentence which makes all the difference to the bankers—and inserts, resting the manuscript on his knees, the provision he himself proposed in the Convention.

Chabot dares not offer Fabre d'Églantine the money, but neither does he dare confess to his principals that he had not had the courage to attempt the bribery; he tells them that Fabre has taken the 100,000 francs. By inter-

polations and erasures Chabot and Delaunay then falsify
the document and pass it on to the office of the Convention for execution.

The Frey brothers had skilfully got Chabot where they
wanted him, after having found in him the man who was
all-powerful in the state, who was "the first Frenchman
after Robespierre". Chabot, son of a cook in Saint-
Geniez-d'Olt, transformed from an unwilling member of
the monastic order of Capuchins into a zealous member of
the Jacobin Club, was a master of the word in speech and
writing, but no posthumous fame was vouchsafed him for
all that: Reactionary historians condemn him as a
Montagnard and Socialist, historians as an accessory in
the Frey bribery affair.

In the Legislative Assembly Chabot, deputy of Loire-
et-Cher had with Basire and Merlin formed a left wing
which was the butt of attacks from the right and ridiculed
in the doggerel:

> Vit-on jamais rien de plus sot
> Que Merlin, Basire et Chabot?
> Connaît-on jamais rien de pire
> Que Chabot, Merlin et Basire?
> Ou jamais rien de plus coquin
> Que Basire, Chabot et Merlin?

On that evening of 9th August, 1792, when the
Faubourg Saint-Antoine rose and marched against the
Tuileries in order to put an end to the monarchy, Chabot
had been one of the leaders of the movement; as representative of the Convention he directed the suppression of
the counter-revolution in Lyon and made a firm stand
against the claims for compensation the landowners dared
to put forward after the abolition of feudal rights. In the
bloody September days he intervened in favour of certain

priests whose integrity was known to him through his own ecclesiastical past. Chabot spoke and voted for the execution of Louis XVI but against the law banishing all Bourbons and all members of the House of Orléans; he had confidence in Duke Philippe Égalité and the Duke's devotion to the cause of liberty. He opposed the dictatorship advocated by Marat and was instrumental in the overthrow of the Girondists, taking active part in the revolution of 31st May, 1793.

Junius Frey glorified that day and its heroes in a pamphlet entitled *Adventures of Father Nicaise or the Anti-Federalist* and Chabot evened the score by quoting from another of Junius Frey's pamphlets *Philosophie Sociale* in one of his speeches and comparing the author with Locke, Socrates and Jesus Christ.

By this time Chabot had long been a frequent guest in the Rue d'Anjou, where the Frey brothers kept open house, so open indeed that the kitchen bills swallowed up 50,000 francs a year. The company at the Freys' table was mixed indeed: sansculottes and countesses, diplomats and freemasons, actresses and racketeers, rubbed shoulders there. One of Frey's friends was Proly, serving as courier to the revolutionary government and reputed to be the illegitimate son of no less a personage than Prince Kaunitz, State Chancellor of Austria. Among those who met in the Frey house were George Wedekind, a physician from Mainz and a friend of George Forster; Saiffert, a lawyer from Saxony who had written an anti-clerical play about Basville, the secretary of the French legation, assassinated in Rome; the deputies Hérault de Séchelles and Julien of Toulouse.

We are indebted to the act of indictment for a description of the Frey house. In the hall a bust of Brutus stood on a bronze pedestal; engravings of the oath in the jeu de paume, of Marat's and Lepeletier's tombs hung on the wall. The furniture was upholstered in green and white striped silk, the silk curtains had a check pattern in the same colours; the mantelpiece was embellished by a fragile clock of blue and white marble, crowned by a Cupid in unglazed Sèvres ware. The inventory further enumerates four easy chairs, two chairs, a mahogany dressing-table, a large mirror, a broad cupboard bearing a portrait of Cicero in relief on a blue marble plate; a four-poster bed of gilded wood, surrounded by curtains patterned in white and yellow and lined with white taffeta.

Léopoldine, the Freys' sister sat coyly in her maiden apartment and never showed herself among her brothers' guests. This quiet girl with the delicate ivory face and the almond-shaped eyes, the raven hair and the golden dowry, was to be the fierce Chabot's wife. In his defence, written during his imprisonment while awaiting judgment, "True story of the marriage between François Chabot and Léopoldine Frey, a refutation of all slanders spread about this matter", Chabot stated that the marriage was brought about by Junius Frey.

"Glandy, one of my best friends and a kinsman of mine, was sent to Paris by his borough in order to obtain compensation from the Convention for the struggle against the bandits in the Lozère province. He stayed with me in the Rue St. Honoré. I wanted to show him round Versailles where I myself had been only once and even that by night, when I fetched the Swiss of the Château-Vieux regiment. I invited the Frey brothers and their ladies to this excursion, as they had been very pleasant to Glandy during my absence. The Frey brothers had more than once mentioned their sister; I thought that she was married and suggested therefore that she and her husband should both come. At this the Freys laughed and said that Léopoldine was only sixteen years old and had been acquainted with no other men except themselves up to the present. During the excursion Glandy fell in love with the maiden. When we called on the Freys, Léopoldine put in an appearance after dinner at our request and played the spinet with so much grace and charm that Glandy's love flared up even more. He asked me to present his suit for Léopoldine's hand. When I thereupon asked Junius Frey whether he intended to marry his sister, he replied that he had already thought that she would make a good wife for me. I said nothing but repeated this answer to Glandy who insisted that I should make a formal proposal of marriage on his behalf. I did this and received this reply from Junius Frey: 'Millionaires have proposed to my sister (Junius gave me their names) but I have refused them all. If the former Duke of Chartres were to ask for her hand in marriage, I would refuse him in the same way. In all France you alone are worthy of the maiden. I respect Glandy as your friend and as a good man, but I cannot let my sister marry him.' At first I was dumbfounded. After a while I observed that Glandy was the owner of a prosperous business, while I possessed nothing save the very insecure pension of a former Capuchin. Frey answered: 'If you had more, you would never get my sister, for in that case you would be corrupt and counter-revolutionary. I am giving you a dowry of 200,000 livres with my sister. Should you at any time betray the cause of the people, you would lose my friendship and never inherit any of my fortune. For if you married Léopoldine, I would remain a bachelor and you would be the head of our family in France. My brother Emanuel is impotent, he can never become a father.' "

Chabot allegedly asked for time to make up his mind, at first twenty-four hours and then another respite of twelve hours, during which his fellow-clubmen insistently advised him to disprove by his marriage the rumours which made him out to be a libertine.

On the 27th of September, 1793, Chabot moved to the house in the Rue d'Anjou in order to escape the vengeance of his former mistress Juliette Berger, whom he feared. In this he was right: she moved heaven and earth against him and on the 30th of September Chabot already considered it necessary to protect himself by a speech, in which he warned in general terms against a conspiracy of women who intended to slander members of the Convention.

Three days later he announced his betrothal in the meeting-hall of the Jacobin club. He declared that he wished to renounce the vice of inconstancy and to settle down; he stressed his own poverty and frugality but—with a view to forestalling any subsequent reproach of having enriched himself by illegal means—he also emphasized the fact that his bride-to-be was by no means without a dowry. The wedding was to take place, without the intervention of a priest, at eight o'clock in the morning, in order not to make Chabot late for the morning session of the Convention.

He invited the members of the club to come to the wedding, but the invitation met with an icy reception. Was it only his imagination, or was it reality, that one of his fellow-clubmen began to hum the song heard until then only from right-wingers:

> "Vit-on jamais rien de plus sot
> Que Merlin, Basire et Chabot?"

Next day the paper *Annales de la République Française* published this paragraph—obviously inspired by Frey—about "the bride of the representative of the sovereign people":

"The family of Léopoldine Frey-Minaires has its origin in Bohemia; she is of the Jewish faith and not of that of the Moravian Brethren, as has been alleged. The founder of

the Frey line had made considerable purchases on behalf
of the Queen of Hungary during the Seven Years' War, so
that the court of Vienna was a debtor to the family to the
extent of two millions. As the Empress was very anxious
to assist the spread of the Catholic religion in her domains,
Léopoldine's father was persuaded to renounce the
Jewish faith and embrace the Roman Catholic religion
with the result that the Empress granted him, in lieu of
payment, the fine manor of Found-Schomberg, valued at
more than two millions, and it is there that the charming
Léopoldine was born."

But the disparaging comments were not silenced; men
spoke mockingly of "Chabot's Austrian", with a trans-
parent allusion to Louis XVI's wife; men said that Frey's
nephew was in fact his son and that the boy's entry into
the revolutionary army had espionage for its object and
that Léopoldine herself came straight from the harem of
the Emperor of Austria. Chabot later alleged that
Delaunay had threatened him with repeating all these
calumnies publicly from the rostrum of the National
Assembly if Chabot refused to take part in falsifying the
decree relating to the dissolution of the Compagnie des
Indes. The truth is that Chabot himself was aware of the
incongruity of a representative of the people in a revolutionary republic being closely related to a banker.

On the 20th of Brumaire of the Year II (November
1793) Philippeaux made a violent speech in the Convention, demanding that its members should turn their
severity in the first place against themselves: "I move that
every member be required to submit a statement showing
how much he possessed before the revolution and how
great his fortune is now. Whoever does not supply such a
statement in precise form within ten days, should be
arrested immediately and punished as a traitor." Basire,
Chabot—yes, he above all—and Julien of Toulouse spoke

against the motion and obtained the concession that the motion was passed with the addendum, that each member, before he can be arrested, must be given an opportunity of defending himself in the Convention.

One day later, the Jacobin club discussed Chabot's speech, described the addendum as being contrary to the will of the people and decided to send a deputation to the Convention. There Chabot was reproached in violent terms, although he declared that he regretted the attitude he had taken up three days before; meanwhile men inveighed against the suspect Austrian woman, his wife, and her shady relatives.

The Frey brothers, who were present at the sitting would not but hear how they were regarded by the people of Paris—it was said that before their sister's marriage they cut a very poor figure indeed, but now her chambermaid was better dressed than the lady of the house had been before her marriage. When the Frey house, like the houses of all foreign bankers, was searched and the doors sealed—a measure revoked on Chabot's intervention—the house now valued at 700,000 livres had contained no household linen and all cupboards had been bare.

"Spies are living under your roof, Citizen Chabot!" Fresh abuse rained down on Chabot, whose guilt was as yet merely an instinctive suspicion. Desperate, he implored "all well-intentioned citizens" to help him expose the slanderers, but the answer was a burst of jeering; then the demand was voiced that the expression "slanderer" be censured from the chair. Chabot staggered from the hall, he already felt the sharp-edged iron of Citizen Guillotin irresistibly descending on his neck. No one could save him now.

No one? Chabot hoped that Robespierre might do so. After a sleepless night he hurried to him early in the morning. The mightiest man in France received the second mightiest in a chamber that contained nothing but a table, four chairs, a mattress and many books. Chabot had in his pocket the bundle of 100,000 francs with which he was to have dissuaded Fabre d'Églantine from tabling his motion for the complete dissolution of the Compagnie des Indes. Stammering and stuttering, he reported to Robespierre the existence of a great conspiracy which he, Chabot, could expose down to its last ramifications if he could remain in touch with the conspirators. Robespierre referred him to the Comité de Salut Public where his statement about the alleged conspiracy was placed on record but the authorization demanded by Chabot to cover his further connection with the conspirators was refused.

Only one more day did he spend at liberty, then he was arrested and after him one by one all those he had accused and many others suspected of corruption, debauchery and counter-revolutionary activities, including the innocent Fabre d'Églantine who was a friend of Danton and Desmoulins. The Frey brothers, taken into custody on the 3rd of Frimaire of the Year II (the twenty-third of November 1793) were detained in the prison of Sainte-Pélagie and their sister Léopoldine in the prison of the English Ladies. "I thank providence" wrote Chabot from the prison of the Luxembourg to the Comité de Salut Public, "that you have at last made up your minds to take my two brothers-in-law into custody. I consider them as spotless as the sun—they are honest Jacobins. Were they anything else they would have to be regarded as the greatest dissemblers in the universe."

That was precisely what Robespierre did take them for. In his papers one finds the following note about Junius Frey:

"Ever since the first days of the revolution two scoundrels whose perfect art of dissimulation make them suitable instruments in the hands of the tyrants, have been living in Paris. One of them has added to his assumed surname the first name of the man who was the author of freedom in Rome. Every patriot with whom he entered into relations ever found him at home with a pen in his hand, immersed in meditation on the rights of man or studying the works of Plutarch and Rousseau. The severe exterior and the revolutionary attire of this new Junius conformed perfectly to the conceptions about so momentous a character: his philosophical haircut and the red cap rammed onto his savant head guaranteed the purity of his patriotic sentiments in the eyes of everyone."

Chabot made application for the release of his innocent wife and this request was granted. The others, even those most powerful in the past, remained in strictest confinement for more than six months. At the end of them Chabot realized that his cause was hopeless, he took poison, but even that did not kill him, did not save him from the ultimate disgrace; he was carried into court and to the scaffold like those others whom he had brought down in his fall and who had brought him down in theirs: the Frey brothers.

They had not been long in France, the fatal brothers. They made their first appearance at the end of 1792 in Strasbourg. It was the beginning of the war and they took up the cudgels there for Thibault de Laveaux against his clerical enemies who had brought him before the courts. Jean Charles Thibault de Laveaux was a philologist, the originator of comparative grammar, friend and biographer of Frederick of Prussia, whose favour he had renounced in order to carry the revolutionary doctrine from Alsace to the East as editor of the *Courier du Bas-Rhin*. He won his case against the clericals of Strasbourg whereupon the Freys had a medal struck with the inscription "In Memory of the victory won by the Jacobins over the

c

Feuillants" and made a not inconsiderable contribution to the equipment of the revolutionary army. The Prince of Hesse having adhered to the cause of the French revolution, the brothers presented him with a sword of honour and the *Courier du Bas-Rhin* praised the generosity of the new-fledged Citizens Frey. But even then a journalist named Chairoux already wanted to know who these foreigners were who had allegedly hurried to Strasbourg out of enthusiasm for the cause of freedom, these alleged aristocrats, these alleged millionaires whose real names were unknown, whose origins were unknown, whose intentions were unknown.

Perhaps these questions frightened the Frey brothers. They wanted to go to Paris. Thibault de Laveaux was just going there to take over the editorship of the *Journal de la Montagne* and the revolutionary Prince of Hesse travelled in the same coach—a good opportunity for the Freys to join them and thus stage a good entry to the capital for themselves. They arrived as the attack on the Tuileries was taking place and the brothers immediately found a way to get their participation in this revolutionary action officially confirmed. More than that—when a fortnight later the Legislative Assembly debated the motion to honour great revolutionary thinkers of foreign countries by granting them French citizenship, Deputy Boussac proposed four German thinkers: Wieland, Voss and—the Frey brothers. None of the four met with the approval of Rühl, deputy of the Lower Rhine, who sponsored the motion. He proposed Friedrich Schiller and no one else— Schiller, who was soon to prove how mistaken it was to regard him as a revolutionary, Schiller who composed the "Song of the Bell" that eulogium of the Philistines, that song of hate against the revolt of the underdog.

Still, the Assembly is to be honoured for not having honoured the Frey brothers, who now had to seek French

citizenship by other means. On the day on which France
declared herself a republic, the Freys adopted an orphan
child and a blind old woman; the Tuileries section cele-
brated the great event by the light of torches donated by
the Citizens Frey and the same illustrious citizens paid a
visit to Foreign Minister Lebrun and submitted a plan to
him by means of which the Prussians and the Austrians
could be set at odds and thereby their joint war against
France ended. But all this and their friendship, even
their kinship with the great Chabot did not allay the
suspicions which were rising against them from every
side.

There was one man in France who knew them of old—
Baron von Trenck, an emigré, man of wide-spread fame,
Frederick of Prussia's prisoner. And he said quite openly
that the Frey brothers were Austrian spies. Trenck opposed them everywhere for he believed that it was they
who had prevented his admission to the Jacobin Club.
He certainly blamed them and Chabot for his imprisonment. But when he mounted the scaffold on the 25th of
July, 1794, his two Austrian enemies and their French
brother-in-law had long been lying headless in the
Errancis graveyard.

There were also plenty of anonymous denunciations of
the Frey brothers. One of these has been preserved in the
archives of the Ministry of Foreign Affairs. It was written
by a Girondist and accused the Freys of the one connection they certainly never had: of the connection with
Marat, the most consistent of the French revolution-
aries, and hence of course the most obnoxious to the
anonymous informer. He wrote that the Frey brothers
knew in advance everything Marat was to publish in his
newspaper the next day; in addition, Junius Frey was in
touch with officials of the ministries, especially of the
Ministry for War and had stated that he had proof in his

possession that the Prussians and Austrians would be in Paris within four months.

But it was not until the boil of the Compagnie des Indes burst and Chabot was in prison, that the Frey brothers were arrested and attempts made to discover who and what they had been before they came to France. But what the authorities were able to find out was not very much.

In the newspaper *Le Mercure Universel* Deputy Amar, in disparagement of Chabot, quoted the fact that two of his brother-in-laws, two brothers of Junius Frey, were stationed on the French frontier as Austrian officers in the camp of France's enemies. Diederichs, accused together with Chabot, declared that he had met Junius and Emanuel Frey in Vienna and that Junius Frey had been a favourite with the Emperor Joseph, who liked to discuss philosophical problems with him. They had left Vienna in his (Diederichs') company in the summer of 1791, had been present at the meeting of the princes at Pillnitz and had then visited Dresden, Berlin, and Hamburg; from there he, Diederichs, went to England as their agent, while the Freys betook themselves to Strasbourg, where their sister Léopoldine joined them. Junius' wife Wilhelmina was living in Vienna in grand style. Junius Frey, interrogated about his personal affairs, stated: "All my possessions have been confiscated by the Emperor. My wife is the adopted daughter of a rich man and has two millions at her disposal."

The Archives Nationales preserve the document sent by the police bureau to the Jacobin commissar charged with the investigation. It says:

"Les Frey sont nés juifs sous le nom de Tropousca en Moravie, anoblis sous le nom de Schoenfeld. Ils sont deux frères ici et trois au service de l'Autriche. La comtesse leur soeur a été baptisée il y a trois ans. Il y a encore deux autres soeurs à Vienne dont une seulement a été baptisés et est entretenue par un baron allemand. Frey l'aîné à Paris est marié, sa femme est à Vienne avec deux de ses filles; et un fils de seize ans, qu'il a mis dans l'armée révolutionnaire, lequel il fait passer pour son neveu."

In order to find out more about Frey's past we must search for an aristocrat of the name of Schoenfeld, someone coming from Brno, whose former name was "Tropousca" or something similar. We find him in Wurzbach's *Austrian Dictionary of Biography*. He is a certain:

"Franz Thomas Schoenfeld, born at Brno in Moravia, 1753, of Jewish origin, former name Dobruska. His father Solomon Dobruska was a rich Jew, and renter-in-chief of the imperial tobacco royalties. He wanted his son to be a learned rabbi and he was accordingly given instruction in the Talmud. By chance S. happened to meet another Jew who was engaged in the study of Hebrew poetry and oratory and who acquainted S. with these subjects. Now S. no longer interested himself in the Talmud, and wished to study the humanities. He finally obtained his father's consent to this. He now devoted himself zealously to the study of the classics and the German poets. Among the latter the first to captivate him was Gessner in whom he took so much pleasure that he wanted to become acquainted with other German poets as well. He succeeded in persuading his father to grant him the sum of 1,500 Guldens to buy the books he desired. He pursued with great vigour his studies of the German language—in which he himself attempted to write poetry—as well as those of other living languages, i.e. English, French and Italian. On 17th December, 1773 (this should be 1775) he embraced the Catholic faith in Prague, thereafter assuming the name of his brother who had already become a convert to the same religion in 1769, had adopted the name of Schoenfeld and was serving as an officer in an imperial infantry regiment. S. wrote several volumes of poetry and books on subjects relating to the history of literature. In 1778 S. and his brothers Karl S., sub-lieutenant in the imperial and royal army, Joseph, ensign, Maximilian, Leopold and Emanuel were granted titles of hereditary nobility and the heraldic document relating to this act informs us that Franz Thomas was chief librarian of the famous Garelli Library, together with Denis, serving in the same capacity."

We approached the final sentence with some trepidation, for it might have said that Schoenfeld had died full of years in Vienna and then all our pleasure at our discovery would have been brought to nought. But the final sentence said nothing of the kind. It read:

"Unfortunately I have been unable to discover any details about the cause of his violent death, which—as Rassmann states in his *German Necrology* (Nordhausen 1818, G. W. Happach, 8⁰, 172 pp.) he suffered in Paris together with his brother Emanuel, both being guillotined on the 5th of April 1794."

Biographer Wurzbach thus knows a great deal about the noble Schoenfeld, he knows of the dispute between him and his father, he even knows the exact amount of the allowance made him by his father, but could "unfortunately learn no details" about just one thing, the very thing the reader of this chapter from the history of the French revolution has now learned: the reason why the noble Schoenfeld was guillotined.

Franz Thomas' name was formerly Moses. In December 1774 a book written by him in the Hebrew language was published in Prague. In the preface to this book he mentioned that it was on that day, the 7th of the Chanucah feast, that he had completed his twentieth year. *Sefer Haschaaschuim* (the book of pleasures) is the title of the book by Moses ben Salomon Dobrushka, approved by two rabbis of Prague, Landau and Kassowitz and dedicated to the famous patron of the arts, Joachim Popper of Prague. The book was a glossary and commentary to the Hebrew philosophical work of Jedaja Penin of Béziers; boldly modernistic, the young Dobrushka repeatedly quotes Moses Mendelssohn—at that time proscribed among the Jews as worldly—and deplored that the Jews were neglecting the study of metaphysics.

Before the year was ended in which this Jewish book was published, its author had already received the sacrament of baptism; soon afterwards he was librarian in the Theresianum, a military college for the sons of the court aristocracy; three years later he was granted a title of nobility under the name of an old Bohemian noble family. One of this family lived at this same period in Prague; he was a member of the Society of Jesus and a professor of Prosody at the University, his name was Father Franz Expeditus Schoenfeld, he translated into German the Latin poems of the court poet P. Denis, who is the chief of Moses Dobrushka, and was formerly priest in Breznitz, a little town near Blatna, the birthplace of the woman who was to be the wife of the young scholar Moses Dobrushka.

Chajim of Breznitz was the original name of Joachim von Popper, that patron of the arts to whom the book *Sefer Haschaaschuim* was dedicated. He died childless in Prague in the year 1795 and is buried in the old Jewish cemetery at Vinohrady-Zizkow side by side with his wife Reizl, daughter of that Zecharja Joss who was killed in the Prague pogrom which occurred on the 27th of November 1744. Mrs. Popper's only brother was Isaac Juda Joss who had two children, Simon Gottfried and Elke. This Simon Gottfried was disinherited by his rich uncle Popper for stealing or misusing a blank power of attorney, but the same uncle adopted Elke Joss and when she married Moses Dobrushka, the future Junius Frey, Popper (the "rich man" of the Paris investigation) assigned to her a part of his immense fortune; but when she and her husband embraced the Christian faith, and she was henceforth to be called Wilhelmine Schoenfeld, the uncle annulled this legacy.

More than twenty years later, when the nephew-in-law had long been guillotined on the Place de la Révolution in Paris and the uncle had passed away in his house in the Prague High Street, a long lawsuit was fought out, with Joachim von Popper's estate as the prize, between the widow of the guillotined Frey and a relative, Abraham Duschenes, who had been made residuary legatee of the Popper fortune, and who immediately upon receipt of his inheritance had embraced the Christian faith and assumed the name of Andrew Dusensi. Regarding Junius Frey's origins, the registry in Brno discloses that our Jacobin was the second of the twelve children born to Salomon Dobrushka (born 1715, died 1774) renter of the Moravian tobacco royalties and of the Jewish poll-tax and to his wife, Schöndl Katherine Jakobi, who was born in Breslau in 1731 and who died on 17th May, 1791, in Vienna.

The houseful of children dispersed quickly. While old Dobrushka, whose sons were circumcised in the synagogue of Austerlitz, kept the only Jewish prayer-house of Brno in a backyard on the outskirts of that town, his sons and daughters were already on their way to baptism. After the father's death the boys were sent to a military school, got commissions, were granted titles of nobility. And Blümele Dobrushka, or rather Theresia Maria Josefa Eleonore von Schoenfeld even rose to be the mistress of Count Venceslas Paar. The Emperor Joseph ordered her deportation from Vienna to her home parish of Brno in 1787, but what could an Emperor do against a pair of happy lovers; she soon returned and stayed with three of her sisters at Bräunerstrasse No. 1166. She mothered above all her little sister Esther, born in Brno in 1771, baptized in

Vienna in 1791 in the name of Leopoldine Schoenfeld. This was the future Madame Chabot, whose age was slightly decreased by her brother when he gave it as sixteen. Theresia Maria, the mistress of Count Paar, died in Paris in 1808 but we do not know whether she found her little Esther there, the widow of the Jacobin.

Such was the family of Moses Dobrushka, alias Franz Thomas von Schoenfeld, alias Junius Frey, who jumped from the Talmud into German literature, from the Ghetto into the Theresianum, from Uncle Popper to Brother-in-law Chabot, from Catholicism to atheism, who took Elke Joss with him into the world of Austrian aristocracy and his sister and brother into the world of the French revolution and there laid the axe to the foundations of the masonry that fell on him and buried him together with Danton and Desmoulins and Chabot in the cemetery of Errancis.

The fantastic opera of this career thunders from *furioso* to *furioso*, so that it can just as well be played end first, beginning with the last chord of the finale, the burial of the hero and ending with the first bar of the overture, the family history.

CHAPTER THREE

Lower East Side, New York

I F Y O U really want to acquaint yourself with the Jewish
question, you must not fail to study the Lower East Side,
the greatest Jewish settlement of both hemispheres.

If you ask the millions living here why they or their
fathers emigrated from the old world, from Europe, they
will, if they answer your question, lay before you a complete
sampler of eternal persecution; of discriminatory legis-
lation; Jew-baiting; pogroms; hunger; a yearning for
land; a yearning for education; epidemics; economic
crises and God knows what else, quite apart from private
sufferings.

The reasons for emigrating are thus made clear to you
from the start. What is less clear is why these immense
masses of human beings came precisely to this spot and no
other, and why they remain here in preference to all others.
Are there no more comfortable dwellings in America or
better business premises? Why do these Jews all huddle
up here in a heap? They creep into the most antiquated
houses of the most modern city in the world: the "brown-
stones", built in Colonial days for one small family and
never intended to serve in their old age as tenements, with
one or two shops thrown in.

All these people here have escaped from confinement in
one form or another and one must suppose that their
flight from the old to the new was inspired by a longing for
the new, for a freedom without walls and barriers. But
soon one realizes that the freedom they had in mind and
which filled their hearts was a peculiar kind of freedom:
the freedom to continue unhampered and undisturbed
their ancestral crowdedness, their ancient customs and
their traditional family circle and contacts. The new

thing towards which they set out on a perilous and irrevocable voyage was just this old thing.

Purchases for Life.

A unique feature of this business quarter is that many
shops and small workshops do not cater for some permanent, constantly recurring need, but deal in goods, which,
once purchased, suffice the customer for the rest of his
life. And yet there are countless shops all selling such
once-in-a-lifetime goods.

Let us start with what a Jewish human being of the male
sex requires immediately after entering this world: circumcision. Probably a single "Mohel" would suffice to
serve the needs of the whole ghetto, yet there are hundreds
of them. This trade like all others, requires publicity and
so the "Mohel" advertises in the Yiddish press and on the
poster hoardings. A Mohel boasts of countless unsolicited
testimonials from every quarter of the globe, neglecting to
mention, however, what the testimonials are about and
from whom they come. Another has a shop and he has
put watches in the shop-window although he does not sell
watches. If you asked him what the watches were there
for, he would most probably answer you by another question: "What else do you want me to put in the window?"

A shop dealing in devotional accessories offers cases containing the instruments of circumcision but it is doubtful
that it attracts many customers. Those who are engaged
in this sort of tailoring have either brought their gear with
them from the old homeland or if not have inherited it from
their fathers, grandfathers or great-grandfathers who did.

"WHO WANTS A COURSE IN SHOFAR-BLOWING?" asks a
notice in the same shop-window—and so do you. Shofar-
blowing is the art of eliciting long and short blasts from a
recalcitrant ram's horn during the Jewish religious services.

"High discounts" are promised those who are willing to take over a lot of one hundred shofars for re-sale, i.e. who want to become wholesalers in shofars. To whom are these advertisements addressed? Those who have mastered this musical instrument, have done so long ago and would certainly not dream of selling shofars to others and thus breeding competition for themselves.

"Looms for the weaving of *Talisim* (prayer shawls). Patent applied for. Production capacity one hundred per day." are also offered. To whom? There is no place on earth where anyone could sell one hundred prayer-shawls per day. For does not a single one, a gift of father or father-in-law, last a Jew to his dying day?

The pious brides expected to buy the blue velvet squares offered here, then embroider them and make them into a bag for phylactery and prayer-shawl—do they still exist? If such brides still exist and if the bridegrooms still exist who give their bride a carved casket with aromatic spices in order to make it easier for her to get through the fast on the Day of Atonement—they certainly buy such a velvet square and such a casket only once in their lives and that does not justify keeping a stock of such things, not even as much stock as will fill a single shelf in the shop.

The same applies to the ornately framed chromo, as colourful as it is vulgar, inscribed "A Souvenir of my Confirmation". Nor will the boy who needs a coach to enable him to recite his chapter of the *Torah* correctly and impressively on that day ever again need the services of such a teacher nor those of the many hundred other such teachers who advertise them. A pious man may have the Pentateuch inscribed on parchment for his own domestic use or for the synagogue to which he belongs, but he will do so only once in a lifetime and it is out of such non-repetitive commissions that the many hundred *Torah*-writers are to make a living.

Is there really a purchasing public for gold-embroidered *Torah*-cases or even more gold-embroidered cases for the Ark of Covenant? They are very durable! We would believe it, even if there was no certificate of the National Bureau of Standards hanging beside it. In the same shop of devotional accessories we saw a piece of synagogue equipment that is certainly never used in any synagogue or prayer-house of the Lower East Side, though it may perhaps be resorted to in the reformist and assimilist private temples in northern Manhattan, as for instance the Emanu-El temple in Fifth Avenue.

The accessory in question is a silver-framed tablet with three Hebrew blessings printed in Latin script. It is meant to be placed—out of sight of the public and perhaps even of heaven—on the altar-table and its purpose is to assist Jews assimilated to such an extent that when they are called to the *Torah* they do not know the three blessings by heart, nay, cannot even read them off in the Hebrew script.

A non-repetitive deal is also the business transacted with the *shadchen*, here called "Marriage Bureau", who extol their clients male and female in the advertisement columns of the newspaper *Tag*. The marriage brokers do a roaring business but their customers, having taken delivery of a durable partner, never come again.

It's the same thing when you die. A whole industry is given employment, the undertakers, stonemasons, the agents touting for death announcements, the sellers of anniversary-books and many others. But the customers do not come again.

The High Feasts

Between once-in-a-lifetime goods and goods required every day the once-a-year goods, i.e. the requirements for the High Feasts, occupy an intermediate position.

At every step the question is forced upon you: does this world live only by its holidays, does it work only for its days of rest? The shops dealing in devotional accessories all along Eldrich Street are waiting-rooms for the feast-days. Their shopwindows display only feast-day requirements among which should be counted the once-in-a-life-time goods mentioned before, for these, if they are bought, are bought in the festive season. Even Gentile firms and such which have nothing to do with religion, e.g. the Western Union, take the feasts into account. The Western Union advertises suggestions for congratulatory telegrams on its posters; the customer need only give the number of the text chosen, and the address of the recipient and hand twenty-five cents over the counter; then, punctually on the Day of Atonement, some old mortal enemy will receive this telegram: "May the dignity and solemnity of Yom Kippur preserve our old and untroubled friendship as before."

As everywhere else in town and country, branches of the five-and-ten-cent shops of the omnipotent department store trust abound here. But they look different here than elsewhere in town and country, especially when the feast-days are approaching. Woolworth's, the five-and-ten-cent trust, boasts of having this year beaten its own record in the sale of Chanucah-candles, having sold a million of them. How on earth, you ask yourself, how on earth was this record achieved—by propaganda for the Feast of Chanucah, or for Jewish piety in general?

The Easter Sacrifice

By far the most important industrial and commercial article is the unleavened bread for the Easter week. The mass-producers of Matzoth invested in machines and because they have invested in machines, they must produce Matzos beyond the week of Pesach. Thus they pass over the boundaries of the Passover, by calling their Matzos "Wholewheat Matzos" or "Real American Crackers" and announcing to Jewry and Christendom alike that these same crackers are quite indispensible for breakfast throughout the year and an absolute delight at all times.

This, however, contravenes the commandment which enjoins the Jews to eat unleavened bread once a year as a sacrifice in commemoration of the sufferings which the stomachs of their ancestors had to bear during their wanderings in the desert. Hence pious Jewish families would never accept as sacrificial offering a food offered for sale as a delicacy outside the prescribed sacrificial period. Therefore these Matzos are inscribed: "Matzos—strictly chometzdik" which signifies neither more nor less than that this religious food is strictly against the precepts of the religion.

How could the tiny bakery prevail against such competition, even if it boasts the proud inscription "First Independent American Passah Macrons Bakery"? Independent of what? First of what? Is it the first independent, or perhaps absolutely the first Macrons bakery of America?

On the eastern part of Broadway a butcher's shop bears an inscription not to be surpassed by any other butcher's shop: "*Kosher* under the personal supervision of President Roosevelt." An enormous sign proclaims: "Private dwelling of the Rabbi of Bein!" Where else is there a private dwelling with a sign, or a sign with the inscription "Private Dwelling"?

In Henry Street there are several wig shops side by side. After the bridal night the bride cuts off her hair in order that she may not attract any other man—and then dons the euphemistically named "Scheitel" in order to attract as many as she can. The male counterpart of these wig

shops are the kosher barber shops, where no razor touches
the cheek of the bible-observant customer, but only a
depilatory paste.

The Topography of Shops

Each trade is allotted its own region, just as it was in the
old homeland, in the "Gass", on the "Plätzl" or in the
market-place. In no other New York district, be it ever
so exclusively inhabited by Jews, not in Bronxville, not in
the Bronx and not in Flatbush among the successful Jews
who call themselves in a mixture of American and Russian
the "all-rightniki" can one find shops with nothing but
ritual goods. Foodstuffs are an exception, but even these
are by no means as strictly ritual in other districts as on
the Lower East Side, where even the butchers and the
Pastrami-sellers (Jewish substitute for ham) wear the
pious skull-cap.

Up there in quarters teeming with traffic the shopwindows might cause the more opulent passer-by or
neighbour to conceive the idea of buying this or that, but
the Lower East Side is sought only by people with definite
buying intentions. And yet all sellers of the same kind of
goods crowd together here all in a row and even the
dealers in the once-in-a-lifetime goods or once-a-year goods
compete with each other.

But should you ask any of these merchants why he does
not move to an area where there is less competition, you
would invariably get the answer, that he was provided
with *Eytses* and that he had no intention of going into the
Goles again. In explanation be it said that "*eytses*" is advice
and "*goles*" into which he does not want to go *again*, is the
diaspora, the dispersal of Jewry throughout the world.
This dispersal occurred after the destruction of the Temple
in Jerusalem and the Jew, who refers to it, could not

possibly have taken part in it personally, even though he feels as though he had. Or possibly he is referring to the exodus to America which again he may not have undertaken in person—it may have been his father or his grandfather.

CHAPTER FOUR

Shime Kosiner of Unhosht sells a Plot of Land

TO THIS day there are many stories told of the stupidity of Shime Kosiner, a merchant of Unhosht and they all begin with the words: "When a Jew is stupid. . . ."

His stupidity was even more generally known to a wide circle while he was still alive and Mr. Gustav Dub (known as "Red Dub"), rubbed his hands in anticipation when he learned that the projected railway from Prague to Bushtihrad was to pass through a plot of land owned by Shime Kosiner in Unhosht.

Those who knew the excellent connections of Mr. Gustav Dub (known as "Red Dub")—and who did not?!— might have surmised that he himself had induced the railway engineers to make the line run in that direction. But such a supposition would have been incorrect, for had Mr. Gustav Dub (known as "Red Dub") had his fingers—which he had just rubbed—in the pie, he would certainly have had the railway station built precisely on the spot now occupied by the firm of "Simon Kosiner, Groceries". But as it was, Mr. Gustav Dub (known as "Red Dub"), had merely gathered from the—highly confidential—project that the future railway line would brush one corner of the Kosiner house, or rather, not of the house but only of the yard.

It was scarcely ten square yards that the future railway required of Kosiner's yard. But Mr. Gustav Dub (known as "Red Dub") knew that the Prague-Bushtihrad railway company would pay him five hundred Austrian Guldens for that little bit of land, while he hoped to get it off Shime Kosiner for two hundred crowns at the very most. It was this profit of three hundred crowns that Mr. Gustav Dub (known as "Red Dub") discounted as he rubbed his hands gleefully.

He took the road, visited this man and that in Rusyn, Hostiwitz and Yenech, acquiring from them strangely shaped plots cut from their holdings. It was evening by the time he reached Unhosht. "Simon Kosiner, Groceries" was already closed, so that Gustav Dub (known as "Red Dub"), had to go in through the private entrance leading to Kosiner's house.

"My husband is in the shop, writing," said Mrs. Kosiner. "Come again to-morrow. My husband must not be disturbed when he is writing."

This was quite true. Every evening, after the evening meal was over, Shime Kosiner locked himself in, in his shop, and wrote away at his desk. From that moment onwards complete silence had to be observed in the living-room in order that no sound might disturb him as he worked until late at night. But what was it he worked at? No one knew that while Shime Kosiner lived. Even the members of his own family knew only that he had covered ream after ream of finest quality paper, used up huge quantities of J-pens and permanent ink and locked up the manuscript in a drawer to which not even his wife had a key.

Of the contents of this manuscript he told no one anything, but would sometimes throw out a hint by pushing out his lower lip significantly and slowly giving forth such pearls of wisdom as for instance: "Philosophy is a great thing!"

Only after Shime Kosiner's death was the secret compartment opened. It contained, on thousands of sheets of paper, copies of Heine's poem "Lorelei", some written with bold energetic strokes, others with small, delicate one, but all with intricately interlaced initial letters; particularly the curves of the letter I with which the poem begins were intertwined at top and bottom a dozen times. Each copy of the poem was signed with the name of the author: "Simon Kosiner, Unhosht, Post Kladno."

He seemed in general to be very fond of his own name: many hundred sheets, covered on both sides, contained nothing but his autograph. There were Simon Kosiners in round hand, Simon Kosiners in copperplate, Simon Kosiners in italics and in black letter, signatures without indication of place and signatures with "Unhosht" added and signatures with the express indication "Post Kladno".

No doubt this mental activity of Simon Kosiner would have remained a secret even after his death if the family had not decided to sell the entire poetic inheritance for waste paper. As a result one could not buy a piece of cheese or a paper of fruit drops for years in that part of the world without being reminded of Simon Kosiner of Unhosht and "the tale of ancient days which I cannot forget".

Mr. Gustav Dub (known as "Red Dub") had never believed in the importance of Kosiner's urgent nightly labours and therefore he by no means resigned himself to come again the next day as Mrs. Kosiner suggested, when he came that day to Unhosht with the plans of the projected Prague-Bushtihrad railway in his breast pocket and the purpose of buying a corner of ten square yards from Shime Kosiner in his mind. He repeated so often and so loudly his desire of speaking with the head of the house of Kosiner that very same day, that Shime Kosiner finally locked the manuscript of his unfinished poem "Lorelei" in a drawer and opened the door of his spiritual laboratory. The guest could enter the shop.

"I want to buy some land here," Mr. Gustav Dub (known as "Red Dub") began his patter, "and as you, Mr. Kosiner, are known as the shrewdest man in the whole district, I wanted to ask for your advice first of all."

"What do you want to know?" asked Shime, not flattered in the least, as he took it for granted that he was known to be the shrewdest man in the whole district.

Mr. Dub stepped closer to the shop window which was stuffed full of sacks of flour, groats and dried figs and looked out into the landscape. A barrel of salt herrings made itself pungently noticeable. The air was cool and it was growing dark.

"I should like to build myself a little house over there. Do you happen to know who owns that field?"

"A man of the name of Vejvoda, a farmer. He'll sell without question. He has too many fields and not enough money. But you'll have to pay for it."

"Aha, I get you, Mr. Kosiner. All I have to do is pay for it. Very good! If I pay for it, he'll sell and if I don't pay for it, he won't sell."

"That's right! If you don't pay, he won't sell."

Mr. Gustav Dub (known as "Red Dub") nodded his head vigorously. Then he said:

"And how much might this Vejvoda ask for the field?"

"The more money you offer him, the more certain he will be to sell, you can take my word for that, the word of Simon Kosiner of Unhosht."

"Is that so? Very interesting! It was a good thing that I thought of consulting you, Mr. Kosiner."

Kosiner protested modestly: "Well, of course I know the people round here. I always say to my wife: 'If a man is from Unhosht, he can't pull the wool over my eyes.' "

"Very good!" Mr. Gustav Dub (known as "Red Dub") laughed loudly. "Very well said: 'If a man is from Unhosht, he can't pull the wool over my eyes.' Splendidly put. But I think, Mr. Kosiner, that a man can't pull wool over your eyes even if he is not from Unhosht."

"Well, of course, I may have some little knowledge of men."

Mr. Gustav Dub (known as "Red Dub") looked searchingly out of the window.

"There is just one drawback to the matter. I wouldn't like people to overlook me so much. I don't like people on the road to ask 'whose is that villa over there?'" He paused as though deep in thought. "If I could build part of the front into your yard here, then your house would partly screen mine."

"Into my yard?"

"Only a little bit. Perhaps a dozen square yards. Say that bit up to the hencoop."

Mr. Kosiner did not hesitate long—the yard was big enough and it mattered little whether the manure heap and the earth-closet stood in the one corner or the other.

"Why not? If you are willing to pay for it."

"Pay for it, pay for it! I can't pay very much for a little bit of yard, you know."

"That's what *you* say! But I am used to having the manure just there and our closet too—can you see that heart-shaped hole in the closet door—I cut that out myself before I got married, so that my wife should always see how much I love her when she is in there."

"Did you cut that out with your own hands?"

"With these very hands. A cabinet-maker could not have done better, you can't see it properly now, you must have a look at it in the daytime some day."

"A very pretty idea that, really. But it doesn't get us anywhere, so let's talk business: how much do you want for that corner?"

"I couldn't let you have it for less than twelve guldens, it cost me that much myself."

Mr. Gustav Dub (known as "Red Dub") could scarcely keep a straight face, but he did manage to do so because Shime Kosiner was squinting searchingly at him to see whether he was finding the price too high. ("I might let him have it for ten guldens if I must" thought Shime Kosiner.) But Mr. Gustav Dub (known as "Red Dub") had no intention of driving a hard bargain. To earn no less than four hundred and eighty-eight guldens with an outlay of twelve is profit enough. "Because it's you, Mr. Kosiner and because you have cut that heart into the closet door, I agree," he said and held out his hand.

Kosiner slapped his own into it to clinch the bargain but was still afraid that the deal might not come off. "What if you don't buy the field from Vejvoda to-morrow after all?" he asked.

"That won't make any difference. I've given you my hand and it's a deal."

"It's a deal then. When can I have the twelve guldens?"

"We can write the contract straight away and you can get your money on the spot."

"Very good. Let's make the contract straight away and then I can get my money on the spot. I always say to my wife: 'If somebody gives you something, take it; if somebody takes something away from you, yell!'"

"Excellent! Where do you keep your pen and ink?" Mr. Gustav Dub (known as "Red Dub") pulled a form from his pocket, stuck a stamp in the value of fifteen kreutzers on it and started to write. But Kosiner wanted to do that himself, and we, who are acquainted with his passion for writing because we know of the papers in the secret drawer, can understand him quite well.

Mr. Gustav Dub (known as "Red Dub") dictated and Shime Kosiner wrote, overjoyed that he was allowed to write and overjoyed that he was to receive twelve guldens. Without thinking he repeated all the clauses not hitherto mentioned, all the turns of phrase he did not understand at all, all land registry particulars, exact knowledge of which in a contracting party strange to the district did not surprise him in the least, and having repeated them, he put them all down on the paper with his usual intricate flourishes and paraphs.

Dub (dictating): "I, the undersigned Simon Kosiner of Unhosht, sole owner of the plot of land registered in the books of the land registry office under the number 734/c..."

Kosiner (writing): "...registry Office under the number 734/c..."

"...comma, Entry Roman numeral IV, page 39 of the regional land registry..."

"...Roman numeral IV, page 39 of the regional land register..." writes Shime Kosiner and he does not ask himself how it is that the strange visitor knows the land registry number of his, Kosiner's, land.

"...herewith transfer ownership of same this day to Mr. Gustav Dub, real estate agent, of Vinohrady near Prague..."

"...real estate agent..." Shime Kosiner repeats as he writes and this novel description of Mr. Gustav Dub rouses no suspicions in his bosom.

"...for the purchase price of 12 guldens, Twelve Guldens in Austrian currency, the part of my yard adjacent to the plot (Land Registry Nr. 112) belonging to Boleslav Vejvoda, farmer..."

"...land registry Nr. 112 belonging to the Boleslav Vejvoda, farmer..." The question how the visitor happens to know the first name of Farmer Vejvoda does not appear to intrude itself on the writer's mind.

"...comprising an area of ten square yards and declare that even in the event of a special increase in value or in the event of a resale to the Treasury or to a company..."

"...even in the event of a special increase in value or in the event of a resale to the Treasury or to a company..."

"...the imminence of which has been in any case expressly brought to my attention by Mr. Gustav Dub..."

". . . expressly brought to my attention by Mr. Gustav Dub. . . "

". . . I shall not make any claim for compensation or make any protest . . ."

". . . or make any protest . . ."

". . . A corresponding entry in the land registry may thus be made to-morrow by Mr. Gustav Dub at the land registry office at Kladno. Paragraph: In witness whereof . . ."

"What's that?" Shime Kosiner suddenly drew himself up. "What's that?"

Mr. Gustav Dub (known as "Red Dub") repeated: "In witness whereof . . ."

"What? What 'whereof'?"

Mr. Gustav Dub (known as "Red Dub") repeated a second time: "In witness whereof the above declaration was written by me . . ."

Shime Kosiner was very excited: "What's this 'whereof'? What's this 'whereof'?"

Mr. Gustav Dub (known as "Red Dub") controlled an urge to laugh with some difficulty and asked lightly: "You don't know what 'whereof' means, Mr. Kosiner?"

"No, I don't know what it means . . ." He would have gone on but Mr. Gustav Dub (known as "Red Dub") interrupted him soothingly in order to explain that "whereof" was quite a harmless preposition. But Shime Kosiner had jumped to his feet. He would not listen to Mr. Dub, but shouted: "We have said nothing about any 'whereof'! Not a word have we said of anything of the sort! And now you are trying to smuggle this 'whereof' into the contract all of a sudden! What's this 'whereof'?"

"All right, all right." Mr. Gustav Dub, (known as "Red Dub") was quite willing to leave out the offending word. "Then let us write only 'the above declaration has been written by me' . . ."

But by now Shime Kosiner had been made suspicious, he got more and more excited, his excitement turned to anger and finally boiled over:

"We'll write nothing" he yelled and tore up the contract. "What's this 'whereof'?" he cried and banged his fist on the counter. "You tried to get the better of me with that 'whereof', did you? Such a fine gentleman from Prague, and with red hair, too!—Get out of my shop!!"

"But Mr. Kosiner, consider please. . . ."

"Consider? I needn't consider anything, you rogue, you swindler! Out with you!"

Trembling with rage, he stood there with his fists clenched.

"Get out! Or I'll kill you, you scoundrel, you . . . you . . . you jailbird, you!! You . . . you . . . you 'whereof' you!!"

Mr. Gustav Dub (known as "Red Dub") squeezed himself through the door leading into the sitting-room, pale and trembling. He wanted to speak to Mrs. Kosiner, to explain the matter to her, but Shime Kosiner was at his heels, his eyes rolling: "Out, I say! Get out of my house, you red dog, or else. . . ."

What could Mr. Gustav Dub (known as "Red Dub") do but run for it. He ran.

Shime Kosiner returned to the shop, slamming the door behind him. From the drawer he pulled out the fragment of "Lorelei". He wanted to continue writing, but his hand was still trembling. He ran to the shopwindow, flung it open, hurled a two-pound weight into the street in the dark in the general direction in which Mr. Gustav Dub (known as "Red Dub") had disappeared and yelled: "Whereof! I'll teach you to come here with your 'whereof!' "

Then he returned to the table and to the interrupted poem.

The "whereof" was still bothering him and the flourishes were hesitatingly drawn at first, but soon they flowed more freely and at the end of the last verse they were already beautifully full and round, the signature "Simon Kosiner, Unhosht, Post Kladno" had the usual swing and a month later Shime Kosiner sold the ten square yards off one corner of his yard to the Prague-Bushtihrad railway company at the official valuation of two hundred and fifty guldens.

CHAPTER FIVE

The Cabbalistic Arch-Rogue

IT IS BY no means proven that he had expressly acknow-
ledged Sabbathai Zevi, fifteen years younger than himself,
as the Messiah, or that he had actually belonged to the
sect of Sabbathai's followers. Nehemiah Chiya Chayon was
an adventurer in his own right.

He was born in Sarayevo in the year 1650 but he soon
began to lie about his birthplace, claiming to be a native
of Upper Galilee, born there during a pilgrimage made by
his parents into the Holy Land. At the age of nineteen he
again appears in Bosna-Serai and allegedly marries; what
is certain is, that he abducted the female slave of a man
named Molina, and that on a Sabbath.

Some years later he is arrested in Valona for an unknown reason. In Usküb he is appointed rabbi by an
unsuspecting community; destituted very little later, he
disappears from Albania but not from the Balkans; turns
up again in his home town, then in Belgrade, Adrianople,
Leghorn, Saloniki and—at the end of the seventeenth
century—in the cities of Palestine, always as beggar,
private tutor, preacher, merchant, pietist, swindler or
magician by turns.

In 1708 he begins his career as a propagator of religion
by means of an apparently very learned manuscript. But
the rabbi of Smyrna denounces him for a heretic and the
rabbinate of Jerusalem, to which city Chayon repairs,
repudiates him utterly. He now moves to Egypt and
Italy, with little success, although the Venetian rabbinate,
partly through carelessness and partly because of the fear
of exposing themselves as being unable to understand its
cabbalistic mystagogy, grant his pamphlet *Raza Dijechuda*
(The Secret of Ubiquity) their placet; this tract, however,

preaches a trinity (of the Sacred Primeval, the Holy King and the Dame Shechina) which is diametrically opposed to the spirit of the Jewish faith. With a gambler's cynicism the author of the tract dared to incorporate the first lines of a bawdy song "La Bella Margherita" in the exposition of his new doctrine. He must fly from Venice, from Rome, from Ancona, from Leghorn, in which last he is exposed by Joseph Ergas, himself an adept of the Cabbala.

Nowhere can he settle down. In the Balkans he is caught out in dishonest practices and has to fly, in Africa those he tried to deceive intuitively see through him; in Asia Minor he is refuted by reason, from Italy he is driven out. Where could the roving adventurer try his luck once more? In Prague.

The Jews of Prague are strange people. Here knowledge was mixed with mysticism; in no other community pushed so far west are faith and superstition more closely linked. The Chief Rabbi of Prague is David Oppenheim, deeply immersed in the fog of the Cabbala and with bibliophile leanings (his library formed the nucleus of what is now the Bodleian in Oxford) and his son Joseph Oppenheim is even less critically-minded. Naphthali Cohen, too, has found a refuge in Prague, practises conjuration and in his quarters in the rabbinate he keeps a stag's head full of scribbled charms as a protection against fire.

Strange dreamers from Bohemian provincial towns meet here with others from Moravia, where Count Dietrichstein, the Governor, has in vain issued his decrees against the excesses of Sabbathai Zevi's adherents and where the Messianic craze is still epidemic. Much honoured in Prague and regarded as very learned is young Jonathan Eibenschütz, later destined to perturb Jewry throughout the world with his crypto-Sabbataists hocus-pocus. Löbele Prossnitz sticks the name of God cut out in brass foil on his chest and smears it with a phosphorescent substance; in dark conventicles he bares his chest and first the Moravian country Jews, and later the town-dweller Jews of Prague gape reverently at the radiant miracle. Moses Gerson Cohen of Mitava turns up in Prague, studies the Talmud under Eibenschütz, but soon embraces Christianity, takes the name of Karl Anton and now endorses, from the Christian point of view, the worthless amulets which his former teacher Eibenschütz gives to women as a protection against puerperal fever.

Fully sixty-one years old is Nehemiah Chiya Charon, eternal rover, eternal refugee, ever ready for new adventures, when in October 1711, he arrives in Prague, that witches' cauldron of religious occultism and crankdom. Only a few days does he intend to stay, he wants to return to Palestine as soon as possible.

But he stays in Prague more than six months. And why not? He is invited to stay in the house of the Chief Rabbi, who is mostly away from home, and the rabbi's son Joseph Oppenheim, full of enthusiasm, overwhelms the "messenger from Palestine" with homage and attentions. His spiritual credit is ensured by Naphthali Cohen, who endorses the sophistic sermons which Chayon has put on paper during his three months in Prague and which contravene the very essence of the Jewish faith.

David Oppenheim himself also gives the book his approval with date of 9th February, 1712, although he has studied the thick bundle of manuscript written in Hebrew script and plunged in a mystical darkness even less thoroughly than Naphthali, who on 4th November, 1711 had already written a panegyrical preface to another even more heretical book of the newcomer, a book under the title *Power for God*. (Even the highest authorities feel honoured if they figure in print on the first page of a book; and an approval, like a favourable review, is much more

convenient than a rejection which one must first motivate
in detail and which brings nothing but enmity in its train.)
In the case discussed, Naphtali Cohen is not merely
flattered, he is also quite dazzled by the exceptionally
vivid personality and quick-witted sarcasms of this
Cagliostro.

So is everybody else in Prague. Chayon's sermons draw
huge crowds from far and near—especially the young
people admire the witty orator and his occult metaphors;
his speeches hint at blasphemous things of the kind spread
by the widow of Sabbathai Zevi, his alleged son Jacob
Querido-Zevi and their followers in Salonika: that the
sinfulness of the world could be overcome only by an
excess of sin.

Through the intermediary of a disciple who had come
with him from Venice, Chayon spreads the rumour among
his Prague adherents—under the seal of secrecy, of course
—that he can compel the deity to manifest itself to him;
that he is in personal touch with the Prophet Elijah and
with the Lady Shechina (the female member of the
Trinity which he alleges in his teaching); that he has the
power of awakening the dead and of creating new worlds.
There are so many people who believe so much of all this
that Chayon can come out into the open, write amulets
for high fees and play l'hombre in merry company.

He has spent several months in Prague before Naphthali Cohen discovers that he has been tricked; but
Nehemiah Chiya Chayon has not the least intention of
voluntarily renouncing the approval already obtained for
his books. In reply to recriminations because of his sale of
amulets and his blasphemies, he has only quibbles and
blustering to offer, for now he can do without the protection of Rabbi Naphthali, he has plenty of adherents of
his own.

Rehabilitated and accredited, he leaves Prague in the

spring of 1712 and travels to Vienna, Nikolsburg, Prossnitz and then by way of Silesia to Berlin. Here he causes his books to be printed with the approvals he has obtained in Prague by subterfuges. He then moves to Amsterdam, only to unleash trouble and strife between the German and the Portuguese communities. The German Rabbi Zevi Ashkenazy, known as Chacham Zevi and the Jerusalem Talmud-scholar Moses Chages launch an anathema against the writings of Chayon who has meanwhile been received with honours by the Portuguese Jewish community. The Portuguese rabbinate, suspecting envy, malice and unwarranted interference to be the motives behind this condemnation, for their part absolve Chayon from all accusations, ostentatiously overwhelm him with homage, deprive Moses Chages and his family of all subsistence, banish him, drive him out and bait Rabbi Chacham Zevi until he, too, is compelled to leave Amsterdam.

In this internecine struggle which set the Jews of three continents by the ears, the contacts which Chayon had made in Bohemia and Moravia played an important part, but not to his advantage. Distance of space and time have put him in the right perspective, the immediate influence of his undoubtedly suggestive personality gives way to critical recollection and his true quality is now generally recognized in Prague. An anathema against him arrives from Nikolsburg. Naphthali Cohen explains in a message that he has long regretted his approval and describes Chayon's tricks, his infamies and blasphemies. David Oppenheim, Chief Rabbi of Prague also declares that he disapproves of Chayon's heresy. In 1714 Chayon leaves Amsterdam and wanders about in the east for several years.

During his absence a great sabbatarian agitation begins in Podolia. The Sabbatarians send out messengers, chiefly to

Bohemia and Moravia, in order to win fresh adherents for their messianic faith and to enter into contact with old adherents. One of these old adherents is Löbele Prossnitz, who still wears the phosphorescent name of God on his by this time aged breast. Rabbi Jonathan Eibenschütz of Prague is reputed to be another. But when the plan of a great Sabbatarian restoration is brought to light and orthodox Jewry girds its loins for the attack, Jonathan Eibenschütz together with other rabbis and heads of communities pronounces the anathema against the Sabbatarians in the synagogue on 16th September, 1725, the eve of the Day of Atonement.

These are in truth evil days for Nehemiah Chiya Chayon, who, now seventy-five years old, has just returned to Europe to try his luck once more. It appears that this old man, unbroken in energy and vitality, is planning to make himself the head of the Sabbatarian movement. In order to protect himself from persecution, he first goes to Vienna, obtains admission to the imperial palace with the aid of Christian contacts and indicates that his teachings of a Trinity have the object of converting the Jews to Christianity. At other times he claims to be a Moslem. In the end he obtains a safe conduct from the court of Charles VI and so this Wandering Jew roams through Europe in fourfold disguise: as a Turk, as a maker of converts to Catholicism, as a pretender to the Sabbatarian throne and as an orthodox rabbi. In the company of his mistress, he appears in Moravia and seeks to attract adherents, but without success.

The Jews of Prague who had acclaimed him with enthusiasm in days gone by, now refuse him entry to the ghetto. Only Jonathan Eibenschütz's wife and mother-in-law bring him food out to the open street in order to save him from starvation. Chayon sends word to Eibenschütz, begging for help in effecting his reconciliation with Jewry,

E

but the only reply he gets is the advice that he should put an end to his roving.

The Jew of Bosnia wanders on. Starving and begging on the way, he reaches Hanover, where his papers are confiscated; he drags himself on to Berlin, where he threatens to embrace the Christian faith; on again to Amsterdam where he is outlawed and banished, to Altona, where Moses Chages, once fiercely persecuted by him and his Amsterdam followers, now lives as rabbi.   Finally he returns to the East and dies somewhere in North Africa after seventy-six years of a life that was more troubled and troublesome than any other ever was.

His son, baptized, later turns up in Rome as his avenger, accusing the Jews of hostility to Christianity and dragging Jews and Jewish books to the tribunal of the Inquisition. For on both sides religion offers rogues the opportunity of satisfying their desires.

CHAPTER SIX

Ex Odio Fidei

O N E   T H I N G is certain: the boy Simon Abeles is buried in the Thein church. If one enters the church from the street through the main door, one may find sunk into the floor in the right nave, under the choir, the brown grave-slab of some unknown citizen and the verger maintains persistently that the copper coffin of Simon Abeles is under that very slab. According to the old chronicles however, it is supposed to be in the chapel of the transept, on the epistle side of the altar, not far from Tycho de Brahe's tomb, under the marble tablet with its twenty-four lines of Latin text cut into the stone:

"Simon Abeles, a little Jew twelve years old followed God and fled to the Collegium Clementinum of the Society of Jesus for the sake of holy baptism in September of the year 1693; dragged away by treachery from this asylum a few days later, subjected in his home to flattery, threats, maltreatment, starvation and horrible incarceration, he showed himself stronger than all this and died by the hand of his father and his father's friend on February 21st 1694. The dead body, buried in secret, was disinterred on the sixth day and officially examined; until the coffin was closed and sealed the body had no unpleasant smell, it was of a natural colour, with no stiffness, pleasant to see and rose-red blood flowed from it. From the Town Hall of the old town it was carried with splendid funeral trappings, accompanied by a tremendous, deeply moved crowd to this place and here interred on the last day of March 1694."

In the sacristy of the Thein church there is a portrait of the Jewish boy, idealized to look pretty, in a red coat and a white wig, a dress sword at his side, a crucifix in his hand and in a *cartouche* the inscription: "Hic gloriose sepultus est Simon Abeles Catechumenus, ex odio fidei Christianae a proprio parente Hebraeo occisus."

The burial of the Jewish boy in a Christian church occurred during a law case which roused much attention and excitement. The century of the Thirty Years' War of religion was drawing to its close. The grandsons of the rebels, of the executed, the imprisoned and exiled, had learned to accept the new nobility, the new officialdom, the new doctrine, and even the new state language. But deep down in their subconsciousness the feeling of having been defeated and trampled down gnawed at them in the shape of a complex. Did all this really have to happen thus? Look at the Jews: persecuted for many centuries, they have yet preserved their religion and their customs and their language! The brethren of the Society of Jesus who came as religious occupation troops into a country subjected by the force of arms, sensed only too clearly that they would have to prove themselves the apostles of the only true religion to all those who held another faith, i.e. be not only enemies of the Bohemian brethren and other protestants, but also enemies of the Jews. Gustav Freytag read the little tract about the case of Simon Abeles, written by the Jesuit fathers Eder and Christel and published in 1694 under the title "The manful steadfastness of the twelve-year-old boy Simon Abeles" and from it he derived this characterization of the affair:

"Whoever reads this Jesuit report without prejudice, will find certain things in it, which the tellers of the story clearly wish to leave unsaid. And who regards the fanatic murderers with horror, will have little sympathy with the fanatic priests. Through spies and informers, by means of promises, threats and by stirring up the imagination, they seek to gain for their god, who is very unlike the God of the gospels, an army of proselytes who are to be washed clean; with the skill of experienced stage-managers they exploit a sordid murder in order to stage a real tragedy and make use of the dead body of a Jewish boy in order to recommend their religion to Jew and Gentile by pomp, splendour and mass processions and even, if at all possbile, by some miracle. Their fanaticism, supported by the civic authorities and a complaisant law, faces the fanaticism of a despised, persecuted and passionate tribe—with cunning and violence, wickedness and a debased moral sense on both sides."

Freytag's, the historian's, judgment would doubtless have been even more adverse to the Jesuits, if in addition to the private tract of the two brothers of the order, which he regarded as suspect in itself, he had read the official report, published by order of the Emperor Leopold under the title "Processus Inquisitorius, which the Court of Appeals has taken against the two Jews of Prague Lazar Abeles and Löbl Kurzhandel for the murder Ex odio Christianei Fidei of the twelve-year-old boy Simon Abeles, son of the first-named and which for the greater exaltation of the Christian faith and for the fruitful edification of all and sundry has now been put into print together with the relevant chief-inquisitorial documents and other very marvellous and curious matters occurring in connection therewith. Prague, Caspar Zacharius Wussin, Booksellers." In this tract, however great an effort is made to represent the proceedings in the case of Simon Abeles as just and the execution of the accused as well-deserved, Gustav Freytag would have found not only things which "the tellers of the story wish to leave unsaid" but he would have had to draw the unavoidable conclusion that the "fanatical murderers" might not have been murderers at all, but on the contrary victims of a horrible judicial murder *ex odio fidei*.

Numerous as were the accounts given of this case, in none of them was it permitted to put up any sort of defence for the accused, who had not even been granted legal aid at their trial. A hundred years later, in the case of the Huguenots of Toulouse, history repeated itself; as in the case of the Jews of Prague, neither the intention of the son to change his faith, nor the fact of murder was proven and in both cases the fathers fell victims to priest and mob. But while Jean Calas found posthumous rehabilitation through the flaming pamphlet of Voltaire, Lazar Abeles and his friend found no one to come to their defence. Only the indictment itself speaks clearly enough in favour of these two men, both in what it passes over in silence and what it does say, although most unwillingly.

The "Processus Inquisitorius" begins with this sentence:

"On the 25th of February in the year 1694 the worshipful Viceregal Chancellery in Prague received a written but unsigned denunciation relating to a murder committed in the Jewish quarter of Prague on the body of a Jewish child, the detailed contents of which was as follows. . . ."

That the denunciation originated with the Jesuits is obvious at the first glance and finds confirmation in every line. There is a passage, for instance, in which it is said that the boy had declared his readiness to be baptized "to the very reverend Father Andrea Müntzer, sc. Jesu Collegii, here in Prague at S. Clemens Rectore and had repeated the same in the presence of several other Patrum, among them P. William Dworski, P. Johannes Eder and P. Johannes Capeta, earnestly begging for it. . . ." All these facts and names could be known to no one outside the Jesuit college.

As a matter of fact, Father Johann Eder boasts in his pamphlet of having himself induced a minor official of the Viceregal Chancellery, who had been informed of the events in point by a Jew named Joseph, to send in the denunciation. "Having received this news and the Jewish informer having been repeatedly and seriously warned to give a true report, he on the next day wrote down the whole deplorable story in order to hand it in to the worshipful Viceregal Chancellery." This sentence—quite apart from the pronoun "he", used here with true Jesuitic ambiguity—is completely false, for "although he ('he' is Constantine Frenkin, clerk in the Viceregal Chancellery, who has been identified as the author of the written denunciation) has been at the same time strictly enjoined to produce this first Jewish informer, by name Joseph, he has nevertheless not been able to discover the whereabouts of the same." The clerk, however, had been careful not to claim any such intensive questioning or admonition of his alleged source of information, as in that case he would have had to explain why he had not even ascertained the full name of the informer.

The very next day the body is exhumed, and taken to the town hall, several arrests are made (that of the male nurse Hirsch Keffelet, the cemetery overseer Yenuchem Kuranda and two serving-maids) and inquiries set on foot. Rumours are spread throughout the town, which soon is aflame with unrest. The Viceregal Chancellery, in the decree with which it transfers the further pursuit of the inquiry to the Court of Appeal, begs the latter "that all things which may perhaps in hoc passa come to light and become known to the public, should also be brought to the knowledge of this office that it may in each case take in good time the necessary measures to satisfy the proper requirements of the same public." From now onwards the whole affair is under the influence of public opinion, which itself has been stirred up by the zeal of the officials.

In the denunciation on the basis of which the inquiry was set on foot, there was only one definite statement: that the child had been poisoned ". . . miserably put to death by poison given to it in wine." In the course of the investigation—the use of torture during which can be gathered, although no express mention of it is made— Hennele, cook in the Abeles household, kept under arrest in the town hall of the Kleinseite quarter, finally admits that little Simon had lost his life through poison. Up to this time she had said, as had the father and stepmother of the dead child, that it had died of convulsions; but now she says: "I will tell the truth: the father gave him some- thing to eat and then he fell to the ground." To the question what this something had been, she replied: "He gave him a herring."

So here was a confession of guilty knowledge, a con- firmation by an eye-witness that a murder by poison had been perpetrated! The only hitch was that meanwhile it had been found that there was no trace of poison in the body. The statement which had started the investigation was thus shown to be no less false than the statement extorted from the cook.

Nevertheless the two physicians and the two surgeons who performed the autopsy dared not in the face of the officially sponsored prosecution and the already unleashed popular indignation give it as their opinion that death had been due to natural causes. In the short autopsy report which in its irresponsibility seems strangely incon- sistent with the fact that eighty years before an anatomist of such eminence as Jessenius had already lived and work- ed in Prague, the four medical men adduce as their finding "above the left temple a fresh round injury of the size of a groat, due to a blow (Is it mortal? Is it deep? Or only skin-deep? Nothing is said of all this.) and a fracture of the vertebra colli." That means at least two blows, yet the taciturn report concludes with the words: "the boy must have died of a violent blow."

The Court of Appeal, not in the least perturbed by the fact that the denounced and already "proven" murder by poison had obviously not been committed at all, excuses the error "because all that about the poison and the secret burial (the allegation that the boy had been hurriedly buried at night having also been found untrue in the meantime: the burial had been public) could not have been described so accurately and truthfully *in limine* by a stranger, and a Jew not very well known in the Abeles house into the bargain."

It thus appears that "Joseph's" information was wrong because he was not very well known in the house of the secret murder, but this actual fact has nothing to do with the alleged facts—the information laid by the informer is nevertheless accepted at its face value: there must have been a murder whatever the facts indicate! The expert opinion of the medical faculty, demanded "by a most urgent ordinance" lays down that "it must be deduced and assumed that the boy died a violent death." The Jews of Prague ask the investigating authority whether it was not possible that the body had been injured during the exhumation; this question remains unanswered, although it did prompt the authorities to consult the medical faculty on the point.

It is tragicomic to watch the efforts made by the tribunal to explain the discrepancies in the case for the prosecution (e.g. murder by poison and murder by a blunt instrument) while at the same time it seeks to discredit, by the assumption that they are the result of collusion the fact that the testimonies of the accused and of the witnesses for the defence agree perfectly. All the persons arrested testify unanimously and independently of each other that the "wound on the temple" was the remnant of a scab which had been torn off "the which thus to testify even a little boy of eight, who was with them in the house, had been taught and instructed in advance." Thus Lazar Abeles was supposed to have foreseen the exhumation of his son's body and instructed accordingly not only his wife and his servant (who are now both under arrest) but also a little child of the neighbour's, whose questioning he could certainly not have expected!

The accused deny that little Simon had ever run away with the intention of embracing the Christian faith. This ought to have involved the subpoenaing as witnesses of the Jesuit fathers who had obviously made the first complaint and who later claimed to have carried on a regular disputation with the boy on matters of theology. But the Jesuits are not called upon to testify. In any case the alleged escape of the boy is supposed to have occurred four months before and could not therefore have served as motive for the murder. If it had been the intention of assuming escape and murder as proven and connected with each other, it would have been far more reasonable to assume that the child had attempted to run away to escape the ill-treatment meted out to it by a brutal father and had later succumbed to the continuation of such ill-treatment; but even for this there is not the least evidence to be found in the documents of the Processus Inquisitorius.

It is alleged that the child was placed by the Jesuits in the house of a baptized Jew named Kafka and that Lazar Abeles had taken it away from there. This Kafka had however disappeared and the role allotted to him in his absence is most contradictory: once it is alleged that the child was abducted from under his care and at

another time that he had been in collusion with Lazar
Abeles.

But now a new witness takes the stage: a baptized Jewish child, Sarah Uresin by name, who has in this case
assumed the mission of Semael. She is thirteen years old,
crippled in body and—as even the prosecution cannot
conceal—a morally debauched creature whom the Jesuits
would certainly not have tenderly styled "a little maiden"
but as a "shameless Jewish brat", had she been a witness
for the defence. She appears as if by magic. Hear this:

"Whereas the worshipful Collegium of Appeals in
mature consideration of all this, still desired that every
effort be made to provide several further witnesses, in
particular such of the Jewish faith, through which a
confrontatio in contradictorio may be effected (for it had
been repeatedly noted on the occasion of Jewish in-
quisitions that a confrontation, in which one Jew says
something to another Jew's face, has been more effective
in bringing the truth to light than even torture) there
appeared quite unexpectedly a certain little Jewish
maiden, by name Sara Uresin, about thirteen years
old, who had been in a true Christian apprenticeship in
the house of a Christian woman and having heard of
this inquisition from afar, had come of her own accord
and free will. . . ."

And this prompt fulfilment of the court's wishes, by
name Sara Uresin (Father Eder explains her arrival by a
supernatural agency) testifies in front of the Royal
Supreme Court—to which she has found her way quite on
her own—everything the examining magistrates happen
to want to hear at that particular stage of the investigation: that she had a year before served in the same house (!)
just when Simon ran away to get himself baptized; that

Simon's father had said it would be better if the boy died and had then beaten him with a log of wood, until the blood came. The girl is confronted with Lazar Abeles. "May God punish me if I ever saw this girl before" cries Lazar Abeles. Nevertheless the "little maiden" repeats to his face everything she had said before, "quite steadfastly and boldly, without fear or reluctance". ·

After this unsuccessful confrontation Lazar Abeles is "led back to his former place of confinement, in the tower of the town hall, close to the clock, well pinioned by both hands and one leg."

A few hours later he is found strangled.

Justice cannot avoid expressing surprise at this deed, which it describes as suicide. For in the first place the "little Jewish maiden had not been able to say anything to his face except a few preliminaria about the Christian Catholic zeal of the boy" and secondly, suicide is a somewhat difficult feat for a prisoner so closely watched and closely fettered. He is said to "have taken off his belt with which the Jews are wont to gird their body, tied the same to a double iron grating high up, having reached the same by means of a log of wood, and having put his neck through it, hanged or rather strangled himself." It appears, so says the memorandum, that the quite unimportant testimony of the girl Uresin "had so touched his wanton and savage heart" that he killed himself.

Although thus the memorandum states that there was active repentance, this fact does not protect the dead body from being condemned. The dead man is pronounced guilty and the sentence carried out, which is that his heart be torn out, and beaten about his mouth and then the body quartered and burned at the stake.

Abeles' wife and his serving-maid Hennele are not told of the death of the chief accused. Despite threats and the pretence that Lazar Abeles had confessed everything, they still protest his and their own innocence. The "little maiden, clad in private in Jewish clothing" is confronted with the maid, who now agrees to everything the child says and is finally made to say that the father had killed the boy. He had done so by giving him poison. The next step is to confront the maid and Mrs. Leah Abeles, who had had a heart attack the previous night. Mrs. Abeles, seeing that the maid had already been driven to testify against her husband, although she knows the charge to be untrue, realizes that all is lost. In order to save her husband, whose death is unknown to her, she states that another man whose name is Löbl Kurzhandel, and who is no longer in Prague, had throttled the child.

Kurzhandel is arrested in Manetin and the proceedings against him run their course, while the boy Simon publicly lies in state with unprecedented pomp, as a Christian baptized "in proprio sangue", as ordered by Archbishop Hans Friedrich von Walkstein on the advice of the divines and canons. On 25th March, 1694 "in ipso festo Simoni Tridentini pueri, aeque a Judaeis martyrisati" a commission fixes the place where the child is to be interred.

One week later the funeral takes place and the body, buried on 22nd February in the Jewish cemetery, exhumed five days later and kept lying in state in the town hall for thirty days, is officially found to be without any unpleasant odour whatever. The second test of beatitude also turns out to be positive: ". . . as also the mortal wounds received on the broken neck always and ever unceasingly threw up the most fresh and beautiful blood like a fountainhead and those present took the opportunity of attempting (attempting!) to soak their kerchiefs in this running blood, an example followed even by a chirurgeon adhering to the evangelical religion!"

Löbl Kurzhandel, against whom not even the shadow of any evidence can be found in the documents of the case,

is condemned to death on the 19th of April 1694. As for
the treatment he had been given, that is evident from a
decree directed by the Emperor Leopold to the Royal
Court of Appeals: "The enclosure (a complaint) brings to
your notice among other things that the Jew Löbl Süsel
Kurzhandel of Prague, condemned by you to death had
not been permitted, either in his own person or any of his
friends, to receive any copy of the sentence passed on him,
nor had any legal aid been granted him ex officio." The
Emperor decrees that the rules of legal procedure should
be adhered to, the execution postponed for the time being
and measures taken "that the life of the condemned man
be not shortened in carceribus, as it is alleged to have
happened with his accomplice."

The Court of Appeal answers the Emperor, alleging
that the prisoner is merely attempting to cause delay,
whereupon Leopold "in this most distressful criminal
affair" accords Kurzhandel a respite of fourteen days in
which to appeal and finally confirms the death sentence:
"Seeing that the speedy execution of the same is much
desired by the public, it is to be carried out on the person
of the delinquent without delay and further respite."

Unclothed, bound to the three-edged breaking-irons
which are to shatter his limbs, he stands on the scaffold in
order that "thirty odd" blows of the eighty-pound wheel
may sever his thighs and calves and crush his chest. A
Jesuit father incessantly and loudly exhorts the malefactor
to embrace the Christian faith; after the eleventh blow of
the wheel Kurzhandel is said to have answered in the
affirmative; he is now baptized and re-named Johannes,
after which the executioner bandages his eyes and then he
"receives the last mortal blow on his neck, and bereft of
his senses and bleeding strongly from nose and mouth,
after two further blows blessedly passes on to the Lord, to
the great admiration of all present, who could not laud

and praise the miracle-working hand of God and His inscrutable mercy enough." The former "stubborn murderer" Löbl Kurzhandel is buried in the church of St. Paul as a "penitent Catholic Christian" under the name of Johannes.

CHAPTER SEVEN

Bible and Babel in the New World

T H E F I R S T man to perceive the similarity of religions was not one of the evangelists, but one of the prospective converts. This one was the Mexican ruler Montezuma.

On 9th November, 1519, the day after the entry of the conquistadores into the Mexican capital, Cortez begins in the royal palace his wooing of Montezuma, interpreted by the beautiful Malinche. Cortez eagerly explains how God created the world and the first human beings out of chaos —being quite unaware of the fact that the Indian history of creation teaches the same thing. In poetic terms he praises the colourful delights of Paradise—not knowing that his imagination lagged far behind the reality of Montezuma's wonderful garden. He reveals the mystery of the mass in which the body of the Saviour is eaten—in complete ignorance of the fact that the Aztec sacrificial rites contain similar allegories. Cortez exhorts the king to adore the holy cross, oblivious that he had found holy crosses in the land when he landed.

He waited impatiently for Montezuma's answer, for of this answer all was to be hoped or all to be feared. What Cortez did not expect was that the ruler of the "idolaters" would answer that these doctrines were familiar to him of old, especially the one about the creation of the world. He and his people had been taught to believe the same from time immemorial.*

The conquerors who in Spain persecuted and exterminated the Jews, could find no better way of vilifying the Indian religion in the eyes of the authorities at home than by connecting it with the Jewish religion. Had there been

* Bernal Diaz: *Historia de la Conquista*, Chapter 90. "Y en eso de la creacion del mundo asi lo tenemos creido muchos tiempos pasados."

80

no affinities between the two, the Spaniards would have invented them. But as there were affinities in plenty, what they did was to speculate as to when Judaism had come to Mexico.

In the centuries which have passed since the *conquista* the most contradictory opinions were put forward on this point by various scholars; each champion of some theory misrepresented all the others or passed them over in silence and it is not easy to disentangle the confusion.

Theory Number One rejects the assumption that the analogies between the religions are due to importation from the old world and holds that all old religions were built up independently of each other and yet resembling each other; the basic work expressing this concept are the *Lectures on the origin and growth of Religion* published around 1880 by the English Professor Max Mueller, a son of the German poet Wilhelm Mueller and a grandson of Basedow.

But even before that, even orthodox students of the religions had asked themselves the question: had Adam really been the first man in every continent. For had he been that if only in his own part of the world, how could his son then marry a daughter of the land? But on the one hand this is what the Bible says and on the other hand it goes without saying, since were it otherwise (if one excludes incest between Eve and Cain), the human race would have been extinct in its second generation. Several authors, by the way, regard it as more or less a foregone conclusion that Adam was a redskin.*

Alexander von Humboldt thought that the Mexican tribal religions were primordial and came into being inde-

---

* Ignatius Donelly: "Atlantis, an antediluvian world". "Adam seems to have belonged to the red-skinned race, as the origins of his name indicate. . . . The words Adôm and Adam mean 'red' and 'reddish' in Aramaic. . . ."

F

pendently of the religions of the old world. Humboldt says:

> "The religious rites, dogmas and traditions which occupied the minds of the first Spanish missionaries had without a doubt already been in existence in Mexico since the arrival of the Toltecs and thus three or four centuries before the Norsemen sailed to the east coast of the new continent. . . . If one applies sound critical methods to the problem, one finds nothing among the Americans that would give us reason to believe that Asiatic peoples spread into the newer continent after the foundation of the Christian religion. I am, however, far removed from denying the possibility of such later communications. . . ."

Theory Number Two maintains that America was populated by the survivors of the Deluge. Here the question arises whether the flood after which the Jews landed on American soil from Noah's ark was the Biblical flood or the Mexican. For the Indian religions also know of a Deluge with a rescuing raft and two birds sent out one after the other to ascertain the level of the waters.

According to Bolivian scholars Father Noah was an Indio, Noke by name and one of his descendants is stated to have written a report about the great flood disaster in the Aymara language on the rocks of the Bolivian table-land in the year 2384 B.C. (This is probably the inscription on the hills lining the banks of the river Caura, about which Humboldt heard on his journeys between the Orinoco and the Amazon.) "The natives say that their ancestors had come up to the peaks of these hills in their boats at the time of the great floods; and that at that time the stone had been so soft that men had written signs on it with their fingers."* That Aymara, a language still spoken

* A. V. Humboldt, "An Aztec heiroglyphic manuscript found in the Vatican Library."

around Lake Titicaca, was the first human language, is a view held by many scholars.*

According to the third theory the Jews had come to this other continent after their exodus from Egypt. The wilderness in which they wandered had been the Russo-Asiatic steppe; then they had gone farther over the silted-up or frozen straits to North America and thence southwards. In the documents and traditions of the Aztecs the exodus from Aztlan to Anahuac is described in much the same terms as the exodus from Egypt to the Land of Promise is described in the Books of Moses. Even the dry-shod crossing of the waters occurs in the codices. In the Sahara a Jewish, in the American savannah an Indian god show the migrants the way, by day as a column of smoke, by night as a column of fire.

The wealth of analogies so confused the learned Franciscan, Juan Torquemada (a cousin of the Grand Inquisitor and Jew-persecutor of the same name) that he discovered evidence in the Bible for every stage of the Aztec migration. For this reason his book (*Monarchia Indiana*, Seville, 1615) was mercilessly censored.—It would never have done to lump the Indios, those "unreasonable people" together with the heroes of the Old Testament and thereby with the precursors of the New.

Torquemada's lay fellow-scholar Antonio de Herrera, whom Philip II had sent to New Spain as his historiographer, fulminated like Torquemada against the devil and his intentions of confusing all ideas by means of these parallel wanderings in the desert.†

But not only in Genesis and Exodus have connections with Mexico been found—the same applies to the building

* The Bolivian historian Villamil de Rada maintains that Adam and Eve spoke to each other in the Aymara language.

† A. de Herrera in the third Decade of his *Historia General de las Indias Occidentales*, 1601.

of the Tower of Babel and the subsequent Babylonian captivity. The pan-Babylonians and Anatolianists who maintain that the whole human race came into being in the East and had not scattered over the whole earth until after the little trouble about the sky-scraper project, are contradicted by the fact that the Mexicans had their own Tower of Babel: the pyramid of Cholula.

In 1585 Father Duran, collecting material for his *Historia Antigua de la Nueva Espana* interviewed a hundred-year-old man living in the shadow of this giant edifice and heard from him the old story that the first inhabitants of that region had wanted to reach the sun by means of a tall building. But when the tower had gone up to a height greater than a tower should be, the Lord of the Heavens grew angry and cried: "These earthlings want to climb up to us. Let us scatter them, in order that those who live in the flesh may not come to mix with us!" Immediately gods and demons darted forth in the shape of thunder and lightning and drove the builders away in every direction.

Ixtlixochtli, the pre-Cortesian chronicler tells in his *Relaciones* of a confusion of tongues which had put an end to the building of the tower at Cholula.

Theologians and other scholars had been studying the relationship between the Old Testament and the new world for over three hundred years when Lord Kingsborough appeared on the scene. He devoted his life, his money and his time unreservedly to the propagation of the idea that Indios and Judios were followers of the same religion. For him the book Tecamoxtli, which already regulated the thoughts and actions of the precursors of the Toltecs is no other than the Pentateuch, as shown by its very name; for did not "Teo" mean "divine" in Aztec as in Greek; "amotl" is "paper", "writing" or "book" and "moxtli" . . . was it not as clear as day that it was the same as the name "Moses"? Tecamoxtli, the divine book of Moses.

For Kingsborough the word Mexico could have no other origin than in the word "Messiah". Mesi or Mexi was the Aztec name for the anointed saviour sent by God to lead them into the promised land of Anahuac.

In Kingsborough's days there was no Inquisition in existence any longer and the Church of England has no Index Librorum Prohibitorum. Therefore his work escaped the fate of Juan Torquemada's book. But not even a British nobleman may put Biblical peoples and Indians on a par with impunity. In the *Encyclopaedia Britannica* you will look in vain for a heading "Kingsborough". William Prescott, who often refers to Kingsborough, "that noble man", knows nothing of his life or origins.*

Kingsborough was born in Cork on 16th November, 1795 as Edward King, son of the heir to the Earldom of Kingston. On the succession of his father to the title, little Edward became Viscount Kingsborough. He died on 27th February, 1837, scarcely forty-two years old, after a life devoted to studies of Mexico and of the Bible and the discovery, publication and interpretation of documents, for the reproduction of which he employed the best specialists, painters and etchers of his time. Of his *Antiquities of Mexico* the ninth volume did not appear until several years after his death and the tenth volume was never published.

The nine great folios are kept in the Chief Librarian's office at the Franklin Library in Mexico and it takes the strength of an athlete to carry even one of them down to the reading-room. Even more strength is required to get through the mass of incoherent arguments without getting

* Lord Kingsborough: *Antiquities of Mexico, comprising facsimiles of ancient Mexican paintings and herioglyphs, etc.*" London, Henry G. Bohn.

confused. But for all its craziness the work contains innumerable little-known facts and interesting suggestions.

As for the fourth theory, according to which a part of the ten lost tribes of Israel had saved themselves and their faith by flight to the other side of the Atlantic, it was a certain Aharon Levi who contributed much to the emergence of this theory by claiming in its support that he had discovered an isolated tribe of Jews in South America.

In 1644 Aharon Levi (who had called himself Antonio de Montezinos in Spain) told a group of Portuguese Jews in Amsterdam that during a journey he had undertaken from the Colombian port of Honda into the interior of that country, he had made friends with an Indio, and to this Indio, Francisco by name—but whom his muleteers called "Cacique"—Aharon had confided that he was a Jew of the tribe of Levi, a descendant of Abraham, Isaac and Jacob. At this the Indio had looked at him with suspicion and asked him why he had omitted the name Israel. Surprised, Aharon Levi asked himself how this Indio could know about the theocratic by-name of Jacob and made every effort to regain Francisco's confidence. In this he succeeded so well, that the Indio invited him to go on a journey with him. They marched together on foot from Monday to Saturday, until they came to a river "greater than the Duero". Here the Indio hoisted a cotton cloth on a pole, on which a similar signal was made from a distance. Soon a canoe approached cautiously, bringing three men and a woman, who landed and greeted Francisco with embraces. Then they surrounded Aharon Levi, recited the "Hear Israel" in Hebrew and told him about themselves and their tribe, with Francisco acting as interpreter.

First: "our fathers are Abraham, Isaac and Jacob-Israel." In naming these four names, they raised three fingers. Then they added the name Reuben and raised a fourth finger.

Second: "to those who come to us to live with us, we give land."

Third: "the patriarch Joseph lives in the middle of the sea." In saying this they showed two closed fingers and separated these fingers as they added that he lived in two parts.

Fourth: "very soon we shall go out to see and to walk." The first words they spoke very fast to express how soon it would be and the seeing and striding they indicated by movements of their eyes and feet.

Fifth: "one day we shall all speak"—they illustrated this by uttering the sounds "ba-ba-ba"—"and will go out as though we had sprouted from the earth."

Sixth: "a messenger will come."

Seventh: "in a very short while." Francisco showed in the Spanish manner, with his fingers, how short the time would be.

Eighth: "give us room, so we can perceive." Moving their hands from side to side they gave their visitors to understand "do not tarry long".

Ninth: "HE will send twelve men, who write." They explained that these would be bearded men.

Aharon Levi claimed to have remained three days among these people whom he described in general terms as sun-tanned, long-haired and well-proportioned. Ever fresh canoes came paddling to them and each landed its occupants only after the previous one had left. All in all, Aharon Levi spoke thus with about three hundred men and women but they all only repeated the sentences quoted above, with an almost ritual uniformity.

On the way back Francisco told Aharon Levi that his Indian ancestors had once passed the hunting-grounds of this region and stirred up by their priests, they had attacked the men living here. After the attack was beaten back, the anger of the besieged turned against the trouble-making priests and they were condemned to die. But before the sentence was carried out, one of the priests confided to the tribal elders of the Indios that the attacked settlers were sons of Israel, their God was the true god, everything He had written on His stones was the truth and His people would one day go forth from here to make all mankind happy. "The revelation of the priest" Francisco continued "was handed down among us in this way: only five sons of the tribal elders are permitted to know the secret of the Israelites in the forest and it is they also who have to visit them once every seventy months. It is through these visitors that the settlers learned of the landing of the Spaniards, of the *conquista*."

This rather vague story of Aharon Levi was published in print by the famous Menasseh ben Israel. He, "the Jewish Leibnitz" who was in contact with Christine of Sweden, with Oliver Cromwell and the scholars of his time, lent this story the character of a document by a commentary running to seventy-two paragraphs.*

He begins with a critical presentation of all data relating to the whereabouts of the ten lost tribes of Israel. He disputes the correctness of the opinion that Peru is the legendary land of Ophir, the name of which was turned into Peru or Piro by a transposal of syllables. Nor can Yucatan be regarded as identical with the realm of King

* "Mikwe Yisroel, eso es Esperanza de Israel". Obra con suma curiosidad compuesta por Menasseh ben Israel, teologo y filo-sofo hebreo. Trata del admirable esparzimiento de los diez tribus, y su infallible reduccion con los demas a la patria; con muchos puntos, y historias curiosas, y deolaracion de varias profecias, por el autor rectamente interpretadas. Diri-gido a los Senores Parnassim. dell K. K. de Talmud Torah. En Amsterdam. En las impresion de Samuel ben Israel Soeiro. Ano 5 5410.

Yoktan; it is surprising, however, how well Manasseh ben Israel knows the many analogies existing between the religion of the Mayas and that of the Jews.

The author who for all his quotations from lay and Jesuit authors never forgets the *Torah* obviously leans towards the assumption that parts of the ten tribes escaping from the Babylonian captivity had gone to China and thence over the Behring Straits to America. This is indicated by the prophet Isaiah with the words: "They came to this place from afar, some from the South and some from the East and others from the land of the Sinosim" i.e. of the Chinese. That the Jews whom Aharon Levi had met, had spoken of a patriarch Joseph, accorded with the prophecy that the future Saviour of Israel would be a Messiah who was the son of Joseph.

Nevertheless, Menasseh ben Israel definitely rejects the possibility of the Indios descending from Jews. No people could change its physical characteristics and its traditions into such diametrically opposed traits as those of the Indios and Jews.

The book, written by the Portuguese Menasseh ben Israel in defective Spanish, was printed by Dutchmen in Amsterdam. This fact and the difficulty of obtaining copies of it, explain why even reference books ascribe a totally different content to this book. Thus the great German encyclopaedia *Meyer's Konversationslexicon* says: "Menasseh ben Israel advocated the readmission of the Jews to England by his book *Esperanza de Israel* . . ." although, as we have just seen, the book has nothing whatever to do with this problem.

Much as the Christian missionaries strove to stress the diabolical origin of the analogies between the Bible and the Indian tradition, there was one thing they never dared to affirm: that the Indios had been monotheists. The mere hint of such a thought would have made the "conversion" of the Indians (which was much more like extermination), appear too clearly what it really was.

For this reason the missionaries greatly exaggerated the number of Indio gods and demons, and the millions of idolos were in their eyes proof enough. But were these images really idols? After all, the Aztecs and Mayas were not forbidden to make images for themselves of everything that peopled their lives, of their traditions and their dreams, of princes and saints, of heroes and demons, of beasts of prey and human enemies.

Had the Indios not possessed these sculptures, they might have escaped the reproach of being idolaters, but in that case the suspicion that they were Jews would have been strengthened instead. Scholars who had found only linear ornaments but no figures on the sacred edifices of Mitla, concluded therefrom that the Indios (like the Jews) had been barred by a religious ban from making such images.*

In a private museum in Mexico where countless idolos are exhibited, the owner, Senor Tenenbaum, disputed that they were idols. He said they were in part portraits, in part objets d'art, in part steles or sacrificial gifts, in part educational accessories.†

Six-pointed stars and the bust of a young man with the Shield of David on his forehead, were according to Senor Tenenbaum proof of the identity of the old Indios and the Jews. But of course two interlacing triangles are an obvious ornamental design and the Indios who use wooden Stars of David for the salt to settle upon in the salines of

* W. H. Holmes: *Archaeological Studies among the ancient cities of Mexico.* 1897.

† See my article: "Tenenbaum ur különös muzeuma" (Mr. Tenenbaum's strange museum) in the Hungarian journal *Szabad Magyarország*, Mexico, 1943. Since then Senor Tenenbaum has donated his collection to the Mexican National Museum.

La Concordia, are not descendants of the lost tribes of Israel.*

A glass case inscribed "Tipos hebreos" contained figures with markedly Jewish features. Here were conners of the Talmud, ghetto idiots, rich men and ghetto schnorrers side by side; the same types may also be seen among the Indios living to-day. But in the same way many a European (e.g. Savonarola or Dante) might have been taken for an Indian and other glass cases might be filled with Mongolian, Egyptian, Negroid and God knows what other profiles, all native to Mexican soil.

In every Aztec word Senor Tenenbaum (who likes to stress that all the schooling he ever got was in a ragged-school at Lodz in Poland) has discovered a Hebrew root and he trots out these etymologies with a triumphant wink.

" America" is derived from "Am Erez koj" ("here are people and land"). The name "Azteka" comes from the Hebrew "Aiz toka" which means cotton-grower. "Mexico" is the Hebrew request of the cacique to Cortez that he should completely destroy the tyrannical ruler: "Mecho ko". "Montezuma" is the Hebrew sentence "Mon teh Schema" ("He whose name must not be uttered") "Malcajeto", the mortar in which the maize is crushed, takes its name from the Hebrew "Malcho chat" ("grinding of the wheat"). "Malinche" the Indio girl in the Spanish camp, who was Cortez' interpreter and mistress, Senor Tenenbaum explains, often sneaked away from the camp of the whites in order to spy on the Indios. Everyone would have unsuspectingly given her all the information she wanted, had not vigilant Indios uttered the Hebrew warning: "Male Inche" ("she is one of those").

* Frans Blom: *La estrella de David en Chiapas* (Tribuna Israelita, I.8, Mexico, July, 1945).

"Quetzalcoatl" the Indio god whom certain authors have identified as the patriarch Noah and others again as the apostle Thomas, "unbelieving Thomas",* is for Senor Tenenbaum no less a person than King Solomon himself. It would of course have been quite easy for Solomon to go to Mexico. For had he not shipping lines to bring him gold and spices from across the sea? When King Solomon saw that his country was doomed to destruction--which was roughly about the year 950 B.C.—he simply boarded one of his ships and sailed away with the parting words: "Koais ailjo taul" which means "I am now going away into the world." Under this *nom de plume*, "Quetzalcoatl" he then lived on in Mexico.

A Maya relief in the ruins of Yachilan is interpreted by Senor Tenenbaum as the judgment of Solmon. On this stone it is not two women—as written in the Book of Kings—who dispute the ownership of the surviving child, but three of them. In front of them stands a richly bedeck-ed man, King Solomon himself—unless it is a priest. In his right hand he raises a knife—if it is a knife and not a ritual accessory. In his left hand he holds the child—if it is a child and not the statuette of a god. The name of the site where it was found, Yaxchilan, is identified by Senor Tenenbaum as the Hebrew "Jachtzi scholean" (question: "Is it to be halved?")

If one is that way inclined, one may find a parallel in the codices for every verse of the Bible. Here, as well as there, tradition relates how the first human beings lived in paradise. But in the Indian Garden of Eden the forbidden fruit is no harmless apple, but a banana, the abuse of which the mother of the human race is incited.† Eve for

* This identification is based on the fact that the Aztec word for "twin" is incorporated in the name Quetzalcoatl and that Didymus, the Aramaic name of the Apostle Thomas, also means "twin".

† Abbate Clavijero *Storia Antica del Messico*, Casena, 1780, p. 49.

her part passes on the demonic knowledge to Adam, man and woman commit the sin and cover their no longer blameless bodies.

As in Egypt, ten plagues afflicted the aborigines of Mexico; settling accounts in the jubilee year was the law with Jews and Aztecs alike ; a sort of Jacob's ladder led straight to heaven on both sides of the earth and here as well as there an animal was made to carry away the sins and ills of men.

On the phallic monuments and in the Botturini Codex one may see that Indio boys were circumcised. Senor Tenenbaum had a relief showing how the bandage was to be knotted after a circumcision. The largest circumcised phalli, made of granite, six foot high and three feet in diameter, are in the nunnery of the vestals of Chichen Itza, vowed to eternal chastity.*

A perpetual light illuminated the temples of the Indios and those of the Jews; both nations placed their altars near the east wall, so that the worshippers were facing the rising sun and the Indio priests danced in front of their Ark of the Covenant much as David had danced. A sculpted rock in the village of Huichotla (near Texcoco) represents a man lying prone, on his chest a square breastplate adorned with twelve precious stones; Aaron the High Priest of the Jews wore a similar breastplate, the jewels representing the tribes of Israel.

The Maya tradition contains a variant of the Samson legend: a captive hero breaks with his bare hands the vaulted ceiling of a palace in which he is imprisoned and four hundred of his enemies die under the falling masonry.

Both here and there laws prescribed special purification at marriage, abstention during menstruation, both

---

* Ramon Mena: *Catalogo del Salon Secrete* (Culto al Falo) del Museo Nacional de Mexico, 1926. (The exhibits in this room have since been distributed among other rooms.)

punished adultery by stoning to death and determined down to the smallest details how women must behave on receipt of bad news. The reckoning of time and the calendar were based on the phases of the moon*.

The opinion held by Georg Ebers†, Egyptologist and novelist that Maya art had been influenced by Egyptian art, was amplified by an American, Augustin Le Plongeon, to the effect that there was a passage under the ocean leading from Yucatan to Egypt and it was by this means that a continuous influence was exercised. There could be no other explanation of the fact that the dimensions and the number of steps of Maya pyramids so often coincide with those of the Egyptian pyramids and also with formulas contained in the Cabbala. According to Le Plongeon the hieroglyphics on the Maya obelisks are quotations from the Bible—but neither he nor his disciples adduced an evidence in proof of this allegation.

Until the tunnel running under the Atlantic Ocean and connecting the Yucatan peninsular with North Africa is discovered, the theories of Indian-Jewish identity will remain hypothetical.

* Dr. E. Boudinet: *A Star in the West*. The Indians, like the Jews, begin their time-reckoning with the new moon following the equinox.

† Georg Ebers, 1837-98 was the author of several novels and among other books, of *Egypt and the Pentateuch*, *Through Gosen to Mount Sinai* and *Palestine in Word and Picture*.

CHAPTER EIGHT

Jack Oplatka's Mass

ALTHOUGH the simile is not particularly original, although it may even be qualified as trite, it is still a simile, that crack about the burst egg.

As a rule Jack Oplatka is not given to using similes. As a rule he speaks quite objectively (and not unwillingly) about his struggles and pursuits, his speech interlarded with many technical terms and American slang. It is all absolutely true and quite incredible. Jack is aware of the improbable nature of his adventures and does his best to prove them true by precisely this objectivity, this expert knowledge, correct use of technical terms and general exactitude.

But: "The eye, it lay there on the ground, was just like a spilt, addled egg."

It is always with this simile that he avoids an answer when he is asked why his right eye-socket is empty. When did it happen? "Oh, there was a row. . . . . " Yes, but where? "It was over the big pond."

For he had been in the United States, as one could guess by the way he interlarded his talk with scraps of Americanisms, and he is proud of it. He ran away "over the big pond" while he was quite a small boy and he did so after beating up his teacher. He soon came back again (even now he is only nineteen) and since then he likes to be called Jack (having been called Kobi before), wears padded shoulders, parts his hair in the middle, shaves the back of his neck, wears wide trousers with turn-ups, no braces and no walking-stick. He often talks about "over there" but never mentions why and where his right eye once lay on American soil like a spilt, addled egg.

It would be safe to bet that it had been in a fight with

a "goy", which is a Yiddish word for a Gentile. Oh, Jack is
not a Gentile-hater, far from it! He comes from a pious
Jewish house and he bashfully respects piety in the adherents of other creeds. He respects piety in itself, he is,
if such a word exists, pan-religious, all-pious. He consorts
almost exclusively with Aryans who look upon him as one
of themselves and he is certainly proud of the fact that he
does not look like a Jew, although he is also proud of the
fact that he *is* a Jew. He always protests emphatically if
he is taken for a "shegetz"—only off duty, of course, as
will be seen presently. And how emphatically!

There is only one thing he holds against the Gentiles—
that they think Jews are cowards.

Jack Oplatka considers it his mission to oppose this
false doctrine and turn those who hold it from their de-
lusion. If any remark is made against the Jews in his hearing, if he sees a gesture that might be interpreted as anti-
semitic, this serves him as a welcome excuse for revenge
and a row, for the most violent and brutal refutation of
the opinion that all Jews are cowards. Whether this was
the real reason why he dedicated himself to his propaganda of action, his palpable, tangible crusade of enlight-
enment and thus, as a result of his theory deliberately
turned himself into a ruffian, or whether he evolved, a
posteriori, an ethical justification for what was merely
racial resentment or simply a natural pugnacity, will
sooner or later have to be decided by a psychiatric expert
in a court of law.

Be that as it may, he certainly does not always wait
until a proper opportunity offers for such a refutation-by-
deeds of the slur of cowardice. For instance, he may
suddenly stand up in a café, walk across to a red-faced
sergeant, whose hand peacefully reposes in the lap of his
female companion—or rather strut up to him—ask him
"Who is a stinking Yid?" punch the unsuspecting sergeant

on the nose and throw the place into a turmoil. The sergeant returns the blow. A fight. People take sides. Beermugs fly. Coffee-cups crash. Waitresses scream. Many hands hold down, terror-stricken, a sabre never meant to be taken so seriously. A little blood. Work for the bouncer. Arrests or at least arrest of Jack Oplatka.

He is asked (or not asked): "Why did you start a fight? That sergeant never said a word!"

"That's right. But that 'goy' needn't think a Jew is afraid of him."

As has already been said, he has otherwise no objection to Christians and Christianity. On the contrary, he serves the latter faithfully, which is a thing ordinary people find hard to understand. For instance, Mr. Süss. Once stout Mr. Süss dropped in at the Café Savoy by chance in company with K., a journalist and a friend of Jack Oplatka.

Jack to the journalist: "I'm glad you came. I have something for you. You must put an article in your paper about the state of affairs in the *tumas* of Prague. . . . "

Mr. Süss pricks up his ears. Here's a chance to get an article straight from the horse's mouth. Eager not to miss or misunderstand a single word spoken by the famous Jack Oplatka, he now interposes:

"Excuse me, Mr. Oplatka, what are '*tumas*'?"

An empty eye-socket, peeved by such a display of ignorance, turns towards the curious stranger who is nevertheless informed that *tuma* is a Yiddish word for "church".

"Well, what is the state of affairs in the *tumas* of Prague, Jack?"

"Well, it's like this: as you know I have been working in the past eight months for Janku. . . . "

"For Father Janku, yes, I know. . . . "

"That's it. At St. Henry's. Since Trinity. Before that I was with an undertaker and one day a ministrant got an epileptic fit in the sacristy just before the Missa pro De-
G

functis was due to start, so I put on his surplice and took his place. Since Trinity Sunday I've been the permanent ministrant there, for all that Janku runs St. Henry's school with plenty of schoolboys who would be glad to do it for nothing, just for the sake of the *koved*."

"But why doesn't he let the schoolboys do it?"

"He used to at one time. But I ask you: if he takes the model kids, you know, the pale little boys, they fall ill after a few days if they have to be in church every morning at six. Or else they go to sleep in class afterwards. Can you blame them? Always on the alert for their cue, having to recite all that Latin stuff by heart, strutting about as stiff as a board with the heavy missal on their left arm or carrying the lectern or jug or censer from the epistle side to the gospel side, with the nave of St. Henry's twenty-one feet wide and six steps to the altar; rushing up and down those steps with all sorts of antics—it's no joke for a little boy. But if he takes older, stronger boys to act as ministrants, they play all sorts of tricks in the sacristy—has such a youngster any idea of what a sacred place is, a *sanctuarium*?"

"So you want me to write an article deploring the use of children as ministrants?"

"Oh, no, my boy, I don't care two hoots about that. Though it certainly ought to be banned. But that sort of competition doesn't worry me. Janku knows that he can depend on me. On weekdays, at low mass, I manage all by myself, and on Sundays I act as chief ministrant, I follow the priest with the holy water and the *aspergillum*..."

"Excuse me, Mr. Oplatka, what is an *aspergillum*?"

Jack's right eye bulges, flattered, suspicious and menacing, in the direction of the inquisitive Mr. Süss: "You sonofabitch! D'you think you can make a monkey of me? First you don't understand Yiddish and now you don't understand Catholic..... What is it then you do understand?"

But then, proud of his office and his knowledge, he relents and explains: "An *aspergillum* is a *lulav*, understand? A holy water sprinkler! Well, as I was saying, I carry the *aspergillum* and light the *sanctus* candle at the *Sanctus;* if it is a *Missa Solemnis* with the monstrance exposed, I am the boss of the ministrants and carry the censer. If it's a funeral or a procession, the others wear white sleeveless rochets and carry candles, but I wear a *dalmatica* and walk with the cross at the head of the whole funeral procession .... I am in fact no longer just a ministrant, but a sort of *shlattenshammas*, a second sacristan."

"Yes, but what is it you object to in the *tumas?* What sort of an article shall I write for the paper?"

"Oh yes, I almost forgot! Well, yesterday that Veverka, the verger of St. Henry's, says to me, would I go out to Sharka, to act as ministrant at the mass in St. Andrew's Chapel, he himself will manage at St. Henry's for this once with two boys from the school. Why, I asked him. Then this Veverka tells me a long story about a Chaplain having called who belongs to the Strahow foundation but on Sunday he is to celebrate High Mass in St. Andrew's Chapel and he complained that there was a ministrant there until now, a poor nit-wit who had been doing the job out there for thirty years, but this week he died and everything is upside down there because the chapel has no sacristan and the Chaplain wanted Veverka to come out there and put things straight a bit. But Veverka has no time to take trips to the country and so he promised the Chaplain that he would send me. Would I go? 'All right' I said, 'I'll go.' 'But you'll oversleep, Oplatka—the Mass is at half-past eight, so you would have to get there by eight and it takes nearly an hour to get there.' 'Don't worry' I said, 'I'll sit in the Café Kagoj until seven in the morning and then I'll go out there. The only Mass I could oversleep would be an afternoon one.' "

"Well, and were you there this morning?"

"Of course and don't I wish I hadn't been. We played cards all night and at seven o'clock I was just having a fine run of bad luck. Well, can't be helped, I said to myself, a divine service is a divine service, I left my money in the kitty and went out to Sharka in the most awful mud. As I set foot in the sacristy I knew what I had let myself in for! You never saw such a muddle in all your life. The dust was half an inch thick everywhere. The vestments hadn't been washed for two years at the very least, the flounces torn loose, I had to pin them on because I was afraid they might fall off during Mass. The stole was actually frayed at the edges, on my word of honour! The biretta was dented in on one side. The basin-cloths were just re-folded without being washed. The paten wasn't even covered and the spare wafers for General Communion were quite dusty! How's that for hygiene? I just threw up my hands in horror ! 'Your Reverence!' I said, 'is this supposed to be a house of God? It looks, save your reverence, more like a. . . .' "

"And the Chaplain?"

"What could he do? He felt ashamed in front of me. He tried to convince me that it was only out of charity that he had not dismissed the *meshuggah* ministrant. And he told me a long story that the old ministrant had also made a mess of everything during High Mass: at the last gospel when you are supposed to make the small sign of the cross, he made the big sign and when he went past the altar with the holy of holies in its tabernacle, he genuflected with both knees instead of only one, but as if on purpose, at the *'Domine non sum dignus'* he made only the medium obeisance instead of the deep one. He kept placing the missal with its back towards the middle of the altar instead of its edge. At the second *'Kyrie eleison'* he has to answer *'Christe eleison'* but he, of course, would just parrot *'Kyrie eleison!'* At the *Levate* he knelt down, at the *Flectamus genua* he stood up! And just as he was carrying the bell, he stumbled and . . ."

"Well, all right, and what happened to you?"

"I did my stuff as ministrant. There were quite a lot of people in church, including the landlady of the Smukyrka inn, who sat in the front row. She knows me from the time when I had an affair with Pepcha—at that time I often used to go to dance at the Smukyrka. My word of honour, I was ashamed of myself, serving at a Mass with such utensils! Even the monstrance was tarnished and there was dust between the rays. So after the '*Ite, missa est*' I went to the sacristy and put things straight. I found a tin of brasso, but what good is brass polish without a shammy-leather. Then I had a brainwave—good for my little Yiddish head—I cut up a ragged *cingulum*, an old woollen *cingulum* it was and polished up the censer with it and the *insensorium*, the cover of the missal and the drinking vessels. Then I told the Chaplain that the monstrance would absolutely have to be properly cleaned for once and that I would do that next."

"And did he agree?"

"He wanted to tell me my business! That the *Venerabile* may only be cleaned by a person in greater orders. To that I said that perhaps he wanted me to enter the Cardinal-Archbishop's seminary because of a little dust? So he laughed and I cleaned the monstrance until it shone again and in the end he too gave the *ciborium* a rub or so, to be able to say he had cleaned it. Well, let him, what do I care? Next I went back to the sacristy and tied up the *Ornate* and the *Pluviale* with the *Lavacrum* and the basin-cloths into a bundle so that they could be sent to the convent laundry at Brevnov. I had put everything in order and the job was finished. Then the Chaplain, it's the gospel truth, forked out fifteen coppers for me. . . ."

"What?"

"Yes, fifteen kreutzers for a wage! At first I looked at him to see whether he was *meshuggah*. What's this? I said. I get fifteen kreutzers at St. Henry's, that is to say right in the centre of the town, but to traipse out here in the night, one hour's journey in muck and mud, and I left my game of cards and my money and all and here I've cleaned up everything and you give me fifteen kreutzers? He can't give me any more, he says, the former ministrant didn't get more than fifteen kreutzers either and the money for the ministrants is paid out to the chaplain a quarter in advance and now he could not possibly charge more and he was paying fifteen kreutzers and that was that. At that I lost my temper. Anyone can read the mass, I yelled at him, why you have every word down in the book in front of you, but the ministrant must know it all by heart! If I were to put a cookery book before you instead of the Gospel, you would say 'jam tart' instead of '*Dominus Vobiscum*'. You stand up there nice and comfortable and are waited on, but the ministrant has to jump about like a fool with cap and bells and then you want to pay him such starvation wages on top of it. Is that Christian charity? Roguery, that's what it is!"

"And the chaplain? Did he take that lying down?"

"Of course he too began to yell and curse. And as he cursed me I saw—sad enough that I have to say any such thing about a minister of God—what a mean, coarse nature he had. He used common words such as bastard, filthy swine and suchlike, he told me I was a busybody and asked me whether I thought he could not have managed without me and if the fifteen kreutzers were not enough for me, I could leave them and I knew what I could do with them! Damn my soul, but I lost my temper then and was about to fetch him a couple of good ones, when he began to shout again. Now I knew why he had kept looking at me all the time from the side—for he shouted that he would not be haggled with, he wasn't a filthy Jewish huckster. . . . When he said that . . . you don't.know what it did to me. . . ."

"I know. I know you, Jack."

"Oh no, you don't know what I am like at such a time. At such a time I myself don't know myself. At such a time ten men could not hold me. A policeman might say: 'In the name of the law. . . .' but I would not hear him. Believe it or not, at such times I see only with my right eye and there is a singing in my ears. Well, when he said that about the filthy Jew, I grabbed the heavy altar candelabrum—but he screamed 'Sacrilegium immediatum!' and that was like a miracle—it brought me to my senses.

"Was it that he was frightened in Latin, or perhaps because he spoke to me as one churchman to another—to tell the truth, I myself don't know why—but I know perfectly well what a sacrilegium immediatum is. So in that instant I came to my senses and saw him standing in front of me, his face the colour of the cloth on this billiard-table here and his hands stretched towards me to ward me off. I put the candelabrum down on the table and said slowly: 'Give me another fifteen kreutzers.'

"He put the money on the table without saying a word I took the thirty kreutzers, made the lesser sign of the cross (I know quite well that I should have made the greater sign, but I was so angry) and went away."

Jack emptied his glass of beer at a gulp: "That's the whole story. But I made up my mind on the way back that when I saw you next I would tell you to put in the paper the sort of things that are going on in the *tumas* of Prague, so that matters can be put right there at last."

"You write this: every ministrant is to be paid fifteen kreutzers for a low Mass, twenty for a High Mass on a Sunday or a holiday; for a requiem all the ministrants jointly ten per cent, of whatever fee is paid for the Mass; for chapels in the cemetery or in the suburbs some sort of bonus should be paid, ten kreutzers per mile for example. . . ."

But now Mr. Süss, outraged in his Jewish sentiments, can no longer contain himself. He exclaims:

"How can you act as ministrant, you as a Jew?"

One eyebrow is raised over an empty orbit: "You silly fool, where do you get the idea that I do it as a Jew? Of course I do it as a *goy*."

CHAPTER NINE

Divine Service in Black
Among the Negro Jews of New York

THE SUN has not yet set and hence Harlem is not yet awake. It will take at least another five or six hours before the infernal jitterbugging begins in the night-clubs, with its ecstasy of contortions, rolling eyes, shakings and jerkings, the flinging of arms and wobbling of knees, whirling of partners and gnashing of teeth at an ever-increasing pace, until it subsides in the morning in a breathless panting.

The sky of Harlem is less black as yet than the people under it and one can still see without artificial light. What one does see at this hour are mostly dejected inhabitants. Careworn Negro women form queues before the food shops and shake their heads anxiously as they pay out their coppers. Ancient heads wreathed in curly white hair dip into rubbish bins and pick over their contents. A Negro, slim as a bamboo stem, comes out of one of the thousand pawnshops ; he examines the tuxedo he has just bought as if he would like to go back on the deal. To-night, when he wears the coat while he is doing his tap-dancing, he must make quite a different face.

At every step all along Lennox Avenue one is confronted with the great American problem: the Negro children. They are produced much faster and in greater quantities than white children and this is one production of which the patriots in the United States are not proud. "Danger ahead!" the Fascists cry in the second paragraph of their programme. "In a few years there will be more Negroes than whites in this country and the White House will be turned into a Black House. Who is not afraid of the big black man? Already there are, think of it! ten million niggers."

This quantitative argument is adduced only in the secondary point of attack of the Fascists, in the drive against the black menace. But in the first point, which is Jew-baiting, the opposite explanation must be given, for the Jews constitute scarcely three per cent. of the population of the United States; the argument against them is that their economic power is out of proportion to their numbers.

But we are in Harlem, where so far as we know, there are no Jews, only Negroes; Negroes in such quantities that their posterity fills the quarter to overflowing. The alleged future rulers of the U.S.A., little fuzzy-heads, have already occupied the pavement, are drilling in the roadway and crawl about the shops and workshops.

It must, however, be said that the only weapon with which they are preparing for civil war and the seizure of power, seems to be the fist. Every street-corner is a boxing-ring where two little black boys are having a bout with an audience of the same age and colour cheering them on. "Is it not a disgrace," the Fascist senator from the south asks Congress "that a Negro should be boxing champion of America? To-morrow the President of the United States may well be a Negro too."

A Negro girl, thin as a lath and certainly under the age of consent, runs towards you out of a house: "You want a nice girl?" she asks and adds, to forestall your examination: "I am a nice girl." Perhaps she is. But she has just as little chance of one day becoming the First Lady as one of the white women, who, while the white race still rules, will in a few hours, when all cats are black, be asking you whether you want a nice girl.

Harlem's architecture is of the same type as that of the rest of Manhattan: red brick houses with outjutting porches merely somewhat more battered here than in southern Manhattan. Your eye glides over the brick-red façades of the colonial era, along the signboards and in-scriptions. " Saxophone lessons." "Lotion for de-kinking hair." "Ready-made dentures." "Wooden soles for tap-dancers." After a while your eye tires, you think of some-thing else, as for instance the Negro question or the Jewish question, although the latter is quite out of place here. How on earth did you think of it at all? As you ask yourself this, you become conscious that your eye had just glided over a Jewish star without realizing what it was. Where? You walk back along Lennox Avenue and find the lost star again on the first floor of a corner house on 133rd Street. The two triangles are garishly contoured in blue, white, and mauve, and a sign in the window an-nounces that here the Royal Order of Ethiopian Hebrews Inc. has its seat and holds regular divine services every Friday evening and Saturday morning.

Hm. Ethiopian Hebrews, eh? Is that a designation of origin or the name of a sect? These Hebrews need not of necessity be Jews at all, not even Jew-Christians, Sabba-tarians, Nazarenes, or the like; there are plenty of other sects that keep the Sabbath and the ten commandments. In any case you have never heard of a Royal Order of Jewish persuasion. Ethiopians are black, else they would not live in Harlem. And if they are Negroes, is not that enough, need they set themselves up as target for the Jew-baiters as well?

Having sufficiently meditated this point you decide to take the advice of the bell-caster and see for yourself. It is Friday, although not yet Friday evening in the Harlem sense, nor are you an Ethiopian Hebrew and much less a member of their Royal Order Inc. and scarcely an ob-server of the Ten Commandments. But for all that—why should they have put that inscription in the window, if not to invite the passers-by to come in? Unfortunately there is no bell, but fortunately there is no lock on the door to close it and bar entry, but unfortunately there is no light in the passage and on the stairs. Fortunately you find the door of the synagogue on the first floor but unfortunately it is locked. So you grope your way back downstairs to the passage where, as in every other house in New York, there must be a panel with the names of all lodgers and a bell for each lodger. Fortunately there is a panel and with the aid of a match you may even make out the name W. A. Matthew, by calling a "Hebrew instructor", but unfortunately the bell is missing. So you again pick your way upstairs, but this time you climb higher, until a little metal tube fastened on a slant to a doorpost, a *mezuzah*, notifies you that this is an abode of Jews. A stout negress opens the door; fortunately, unfortunately, she is the *rabbetzin* in person and she conducts you to her spouse.

Rabbi W. A. Matthew is a Negro—the colour of his skin leaves no doubt about this fact. His headgear, the *yermelka*, leaves no doubt about the other fact that he is also a Jew. Black as his face is also the beard that sprouts on it, making his eyes seem the whiter as they meet yours. He distrusts you, who have entered his house thus unannounced, a white-skinned stranger, he distrusts you to the highest degree. You come to ask questions but are first yourself questioned: to what synagogue do you belong? Do you know anyone who knows our community? Have you ever heard anything about our community? Why did you come here anyway?

Your answers seem to contain nothing suspicious. Nevertheless he grunts that the Sabbath is imminent and he has many important matters to attend to, for instance he does not know how he will pay the rent the day after to-morrow and what in fact was it you wanted to know?

In fact you want to know whether his community is a Jewish community?

The answer is pitched high and shrill, is almost a scream. Yes, the community is Jewish, you can have seen that anyway on the window, it is just as Jewish as all other Jewish communities, the white ones. In fact it is much more Jewish than the other Jewish communities, the white ones, because those others are very dubious indeed in point of race through conversions and mixed marriages. "But we" he adds, "we are quite unequivocal and racially pure because our country has from time immemorial been inhabited by Jews and our Emperor bears the title Lion of Judah."

You do not contradict him; on the contrary you appear completely convinced and ask him since when there have been Jewish Negroes.

"I can tell you that. Just exactly since there have been any Jews at all."

For you must know that Sara, wife of the patriarch Abraham, had been the daughter of a Negress. And in a histrionic masterpiece of a phrase, in which horror and delight contend with each other, Rabbi Matthew speaks to me of Sara's twin grandchildren: of Esau, who had been hairy, with a bristling beard, and hence a white man, while Jacob had been endowed with the beautiful smooth skin of the Negro and was forced to disguise himself with a goat's skin in order to fool his blind father that he was not Jacob but Esau. Thus does white and black alternate in the posterity of Jacob, the twelve tribes. King Solomon had a black son by the Queen of Sheba; he was named Menelik; he went away to Egypt and Ethiopia and in memory of him many of Ethiopia's emperors bear this name down to our own days. "We", says Rabbi Matthew, "have all been Jews while we were still in Africa; none of us has been converted to the Jewish faith in America."

All this is polemically stressed and probably directed against any idea that the Jewish Negro community is anything like the many hundred Christian sects existing in the United States, whose members are recruited by missionaries and itinerant preachers. The statement of the Rabbi is also meant to contradict sharply the not unnatural surmise that these Negroes might, in the days of slavery, have adopted the Jewish faith of their owners, i.e. that they come of a good Jewish slave cabin.

You ask the Rabbi how he came by his name of Matthew, was that a usual name in an African Negro kraal?

He answers with that look which is generally accompanied in films by the question: "Smart guy, huh?" But he leaves these accompanying words, unsaid. He only says that he himself comes from West Africa, that he spent his youth there, partly in the British colony of Lagos, partly in Sierra Leone. His father's name was Yehuda ben Benjamin and he was in service with an Englishman whose name was Matthew. It was after this Englishman that Yehuda's son Moses later called himself Matthew, Wentworth Arthur Matthew.

"Most of the members of our community," Rabbi Wentworth Arthur Matthew continues "are of Ethiopian origin, they are Falashas who have adhered to the Jewish faith since time immemorial."

Indeed! The Falashas are the Jews of Abyssinia; there can be no doubt that they are Jews and among their Jewish characteristics is also the fact that they have suffered persecution and attempts to exterminate them and have survived all these. Their worship contains many Israelitic elements but at bottom it differs widely from what it is accepted to call the religion of Moses. Above all Hebrew is, so to speak, Greek to them. The Falashas do not keep the feast of the New Year, nor the Day of Atonement and they begin the New Year with a "transgression", i.e. the feast of Passover. True that on this occasion they sacrifice a lamb and purify, or rather sanctify themselves by means of the ashes of a red cow—a rite recommended in the Pentateuch, but long since forgotten by the Jews of Europe. They regard the Sabbath as the holiest of holidays and believe that it was created before there was a heaven or an earth—that there was chaos to the right and chaos to the left, but in between there was already the loveliest of Sabbaths. The said Sabbath does not, however, appear in their eyes as a bride or as a marriage feast, which the impatient and headstrong bridegroom begins on the eve of the wedding day. For them the Sabbath is a very holy day indeed, but it begins in the morning, like other days.

A very deep-seated difference lies in their birth rites. First of all the black foreskin of a new-born boy is circumcised by a woman and secondly the operation is performed not only on boys but on girls as well (excision of the clitoris).

As you have at one time heard something about these measures, you ask Rabbi Matthew whether they are still customary in New York. By asking this question you have dropped a huge brick! The Rabbi is most emphatic: his community differs in not one iota from any other Jewish community in New York. The *mohel* of their community is a *mohel* of the male sex and he does *not* circumcise girls. Although you assure him that you believe absolutely every word he says, the Rabbi at first remains irate, for the fact that you are acquainted with the dark spots in the ritual of the dark-skinned Jews convinces him more than ever that you are a spy working for some sort of white Jews who deny the existence of Negro Jews.

When a few years ago the Negro Jews of New York collected funds to build a temple, the alliance of New York synagogues warned its members not to contribute to this fund. Thereupon the blacks proceeded against the whites

—paradoxically enough, in a court of law. The bench was composed of non-Jews and decided according to worldly laws, that as both parties observed the same rites, the Negro Jews had as much right to call themselves Jews as any other Jew. To you however this lawsuit seems strange indeed, for you live in a time in which it is precisely proof of *not* being a Jew, even proof of being the result of an act of adultery of one's mother that is worth all sorts of research in registers and of forgery, i.e. is really good value for money.

But now Rabbi Matthew curtly declines to answer any more questions and you find yourself chucked out. But who, oh who, can prevent you from taking part in the evening service? No one can prevent you, although the congregation eyes you with curiosity, suspicion and even hostility. Never mind—think what a sensation it would have caused in the Pinkas-Shool in Prague if a coal-black, raven-black Negro had turned up there one Friday evening among the temple members of long standing.

To tell the truth, the analogy between the Pinkas-Shool in Prague and the Negro synagogue of New York is pretty incomplete. In contradistinction to the Pinkas-Shool, no difference of level and no grating divides the men from the women in New York. They all sit together in the primitive but roomy prayerhouse as they might have sat in slavery times in Uncle Tom's tabernacle. Some, holding books of music in their hands, sit, it is true, on chairs placed around a piano and form a choir. On the wall hangs a portrait of Haile Selassie, the Negus of Abyssinia and its frame contains in addition a letter from his Embassy in the United States, expressing thanks for the gift of one dollar for the defence fund.

Officiating at the altar is your surly friend Rabbi Matthew. Two giants stand on either side of him; their

arms are folded and they look like black archangels leaning on invisible swords.

On the left side, beneath the Ark of Covenant, a special
group is placed. They do not wear the little skullcaps of
the rest of the congregation, but tall, flesh-coloured—i.e.
in this case, black—birettas and are strikingly large, well-
dressed, and pious men in well-pressed trousers. That
they are deserving of the adjective "pious" seems indicated, for they not only know all the prayers by heart, but
also know all the clues for their responses and know when
they have to get up and when they have to sit down. It is a
moment of frightening magnificence, when they unfold
their milk-white, silk-fringed *tallisim* all at precisely the
same instant, so that the shawl is turned the same instant
into a white burnous and is then twisted around the body
to form a mantle with a widely sweeping, almost warlike
gesture. Now they are all in white underneath their ebony
heads.

That these men are the Kohanim, will later become
clear from the sermon, but this conception seems to you to
be incompatible with the one applied to the Kohanim in
the Pinkas synagogue in Prague. There the Kohanim
were gentlemen of the names of Kohn, Kohner, Cohen or
Katz (which latter is an abbreviation of Kohen-zedek)
and these names were their credentials, these names
proved that they descended in direct male line from
Aaron, the first high priest and brother of Moses. It
mattered little there that the *Tallis* hung round their ever-
coughing necks like an old muffler. But here, these black
Kohanim with the white war cloaks can scarcely bear the
names Kohn, Kohner or Katz and resemble the imperious
high priest Aaron (who to the best of our knowledge was a
white man) far more than did the Kohns, Kohners and
Katzes of Prague. The original Falashas who live in
Ethiopia have even eunuchs among their Kohanim—

H

how, you might ask, could the son of such a barren one
prove his own descent from Aaron?

Do not look around so much, for your doing so must
evoke disapproval if not a suspicion of the darkest hue.
You had better pray! The prayer-book which the black
verger has handed to you is very like the one you used as a
boy in the Pinkas-Shool; the words are pronounced
Sephardic fashion but otherwise the *Nigun* of the Negroes
differs in nothing from the cadence and melody of the
white worshippers. Instead of "amen" they say and sing
"Hallelujah—Amen", which is the custom in many
American synagogues.

Only at the very end of the service is a sacrosanct chant
announced, the name of which you have never heard,
although this is of little importance, for you are not an
expert in religious chants. This chant is called "The
Koschat" and it is spelled not in the English way with an
"sh" but German fashion with an "sch", as you ascertain
by peeping into the music of one of the ladies of the choir.
The choir sings with sheets of music in their hands, but
the congregation knows the text by heart; you on the other
hand find yourself to your amazement in the opposite
situation: you do not know the Hebrew words, but the
melody is familiar enough and so you join in at the top of
your voice as though you had sung it in divine service all
your life, you sing "Oh, forsaken am I forsaken, Like a
pebble in the road. . . ."

You think of the dear old author of this song, old Koschat. He was a Gentile and a member of the chorus at the
Imperial Opera House of Vienna, and used to sit all day
in the Café Dobner just opposite the Opera House, at the
table reserved for the musical intelligentsia. All Austria
sang his popular songs, every military band played them,
but his ambition was to be recognized by the ultra-
radical composers such as Hugo Wolf, Gustav Mahler and

Arnold Schönberg. They refused to recognize him, however, to the end. They smiled at his primitive combinations of tone and said mockingly that he had lost his way, wandered from G major to E flat minor and could not get out any more. And alas, it would have not done him any good in their eyes if they had learned that his arch-Carinthian love-song was to serve the Royal Order of Ethiopian Hebrews and observers of the Ten Commandments in New York as the holiest of hymns and bear his name "The Koschat" as a title.

How did you come to talk about this song? Oh yes, it was one of the things you mentioned as you enumerated the oddities which made this Friday evening with the blacks so interesting for you. But there was one more curiosity before that: the sermon. It was directed straight at you, the white sheep in the black fold, if not a wolf in white sheep's clothing. You felt yourself growing ever whiter while the faces turning towards you grew ever more sombre. Rabbi Matthew for his part preached (accompanied by an approving Hallelujah-amen in the middle and at the end of each sentence) about those curious men and spies who came to expose this community as being non-Jews. How evil and malicious were they! ("Hallelujah-Amen.") For instance a man came to him to-day and asked whether women performed the circumcision and whether girls were circumcised same as the boys, the shameless one! ("Hallelujah-Amen.") Eyes flashing with hostility stare at you from every corner of the Negro kraal so that the world goes dark in front of your eyes.

You draw a deep breath when after the final chord of the old familiar Koschat you have run the gauntlet and have passed through the door of the synagogue and stand outside in Harlem, "forsaken like a pebble in the road".

CHAPTER TEN

Lobing, Sub-Editor, Retired

I F O L D Lobing were ever to hear that these four words
are meant to refer to him, he would certainly issue an
energetic denial: his name, he would say, is not Lobing,
and he is not at all retired. Such a statement on his part
would have to be accepted as authentic and undisput-
able, for every man knows best what his own name and
calling is.

Only in the case of Lobing, sub-editor, retired, is this
not correct. He really does not know that his name is
Lobing and that he is a sub-editor, retired.

True, it has not always been thus. For more than forty
years he was a sub-editor on the active list and his name
was Levy. For more than forty times three hundred and
sixty-four nights he presented the news or an expression
of opinion or a demand sometimes indignantly, sometimes
informatively, sometimes enthusiastically, until the copy
occupied exactly two columns of a hundred lines each and
was fit to occupy first place in the paper. In the last third
of the nineteenth century all important and many unimportant events had to submit to subbing by sub-editor
Levy. Each of his leaders was ablaze with an excitement—
highly beneficial to the circulation figures—about the
conduct of this or that foreign state; the reader at the
breakfast table or elsewhere was bound to take it all in
with the slow nod of approval and mutter: "That'll show
'em!!"

Levy was severe, but he was just. True, he flayed the
opponent of the hour without mercy, but at the same time
provided him with plenty of well-intentioned advice,
couched in such dignified, even solemn language that the
anti-European mandarins of the Empress of China, the

French General MacMahon or the planners of the Suez Canal would certainly have taken to heart the *"caveant consules"* which often formed the end of the two hundred lines—had they only had an opportunity of reading Levy's leading article.

They did not read it, however, and have only themselves to blame for the consequences. Apart from these they also deprived themselves of some aesthetic pleasure for Levy was second to none in his ability to fling down a simple statement with force and swing and irony. For instance on the day preceding the battle of Königgraetz, his sharp pen prophesied thus: "Truly never again will the cowardly hordes of the Prussian people, ineluctably fallen into decay, dare attempt to implement the miserably stuttered threats of the foolish windbag Bismarck and raise their rusty weapons against the glorious Monarchy, steeled in victories, whose host, inspired by the lofty spirit of Father Radetzky, would forsooth soon inflict a second Cannae on them. . . ."

Such were the things Levy proclaimed year in and year out for forty years. When, with this end in view, he sat at his desk between nine o'clock and midnight, no one ventured to speak so much as one word to him, for Levy shouted at any interrupter in stentorian tones: "Go away! I must have peace and quiet to get excited in!"

Even hot news pertinent to the subject of the leading article he was creating he accepted during this act of creation only in the event of an absolute emergency. He hated telegraph and telephone and looked upon them as the henchmen of Lucifer, sent out to turn into their opposites the most carefully polished premises of a leading article and thus make nonsense of the irrefutable conclusion drawn from them a minute before.

In respect of innovations which did not seem to constitute a direct menace to the leading article Levy took up a "modern" attitude; even the invention of the motor-car met with his approval, although he did not fail to qualify his praise by the remark: "It can of course never develop into a real means of transport."

There was one thing he hated more than telegraph and telephone: the "devil's pianoforte", the type-setting machine. In the days of hand-setting the complete reconstruction of a leading article had been impossible because of lack of time if for no other reason; the hand compositor needed as much time to set up the copy, as Levy needed to create it. But when the first "devil's pianoforte", the type-setting machine arrived, the security of the leading article was a thing of the past. Every scrap of news, even if it came in ever so late, was pregnant with the possibility of being turned into a leading article. Not, however, by Levy himself. He, who for forty years had left the office every midnight with the assurance that he had provided the world with a correct and statesmanlike appreciation of the position, now repeatedly met with the experience of reading in the morning, in the space reserved for the leading article, something that was by no means identical with what he himself had written the night before.

Another generation of political journalists had appeared upon the scene, who concealed their exaggerated sense of their own importance and their vanity under a mask of cynicism and self-mockery. These slick and nimble fellows enjoyed the patronage of the two new publishers who had taken over the paper after the death of their father and who wanted at all cost to show that things had changed, as a result. Above all they objected to the Jewish names of the office staff, all the Pollaks, Kohns and Levys and so the publishers obtained, in return for certain favours shown to a prime minister, the favour of being permitted to change, in one batch, the names of all their editorial staff.

Old Levy was on this occasion invested with the name of Lobing. But as he continued to call himself "Levy" and as the publishers noticed one day that he consistently signed himself "Levy" in the salary receipt book, they realized that they had forgotten to inform him of his change of name. It was too late now, so they left it at that and also refrained from informing old Levy, whose services as a leader-writer were required ever less frequently and finally not at all, that he had been permanently retired on a pension.

And thus Lobing, retired sub-editor, did not know that his name was Lobing, nor that he was a retired sub-editor.

On the first of every month he drew his pension, which he thought was his salary and spent the time in between in the editorial office, striding through the rooms with severe dignity, ever prepared to write the leader, walking, as it were, on the buskins on which he had formerly accompanied the events of the day to the extent of two hundred lines every day.

At first the youngsters in the office amused themselves by asking his opinion on all sorts of topical matters of which he had not the least idea—and laughing at his stilted answers. But later the joke ceased to be a joke and the old man was left to wander through the rooms in peace and with solemnity. What was going on in his mind no one suspected. Until one summer's day, in 1923, a young sub, out of boredom or mischief, felt the urge to speak to Lobing, and asked him:

"What is your opinion of the abolition of capital punishment?"

Lobing checked his leonine stride, folded his hands behind his back and reacted by asking another question—a question which anyone could guess who had ever read a single one of Lobing's leaders. With eyebrows and voice raised, he inquired:

"Whence has this knowledge come to you?"

"Why, Parliament has decided it."

Lobing raised an admonitory finger: "In connection with which it is well to remember that any change in the constitution or in the laws of this country, if resolved by Parliament, requires first of all the assent of the Emperor."

"What emperor would that be?" asked the surprised newsman.

In a schoolmasterly tone, but yet cautiously avoiding the name of the Emperor, Lobing answered: "Of His Apostolic Majesty the Emperor of Austria, King of Hungary, King of Bohemia. . . . ."

He would certainly have recited the entire Greater Title but the younger colleague did not let him get even to "King of Lodomeria and Illyria" much less to "Prince-Count of the Tyrol, Lord of Görz and Gradiska" or even less to "King of Jerusalem" but interrupted him with a: "But we have no emperor any more!"

"Did I hear aright? No emperor any more? What have we then, if I may ask?"

"A republic, that's what we've got now."

Lobing looked the speaker firmly in the eye: "And since what year of our era is this form of state of a Roman *res publica* as alleged by you, supposed to have been in existence?"

"For the past five years."

Lobing jumped with surprise. "Strange and incredible indeed!" Then he turned on his heel and resumed his pacing in the office with excited strides.

The originator of this conversation stared in amazement at the old man, who once had the job of giving a categoric and detailed appreciation on every event of the day and who now no longer knew even that the war was at an end and that the Austro-Hungarian monarchy had ceased to be. "Perhaps," thought the younger man, "perhaps I have sprung these facts on him too suddenly and tactlessly and have offended him by putting him into the position of revealing an ignorance of which he is ashamed."

He followed old Lobing to the other room in order to soothe him: "But, Mr. Levy, of course you know that we have a republic, you were only poking fun at me, weren't you?"

"No!" Lobing, the retired editor interrupted him. A decade of wrath and bitterness at having been superseded broke through with elemental force: "No, I didn't know, of course not! In this office I am only a fifth wheel on the cart! No one tells *me* anything!"

As he shouted out his anger, he clenched his fists against the enemy who had concealed the most important events from him.

CHAPTER ELEVEN

The Dead Dog and the Living Jew

A HUMAN neck, stiff and wrapped in wrinkly brown skin, was suddenly stretched out towards little Kamilla. Because she was startled, I looked up and caught sight of this strange body, I have not forgotten it ever since. It is a very long time since this meeting frightened the first stirrings of puberty in me. The century had scarcely begun. Little Kamilla was fifteen, two or three months younger than myself. In the city park—where we had met after our return from the summer holidays, at first not by appointment and yet not by chance—one could not kiss or only with difficulties and in the Garden of Paradise where there were no mothers, school-fellows or other acquaintances, there were too many adults prone to smile insolently at a courting couple of such diminutive dimensions.

It was then that we discovered the Jewish graveyard. The people here had long since ceased to smile at or gossip about anyone, they were dead and even the worms they had at one time fed had long since fallen to dust.

A warren of interlacing branches, crazily leaning gravestones, gravemounds and graven sarcophagi formed protective hiding-places for us. In the western half, the most tangled and impenetrable part of this city of the dead, there stood a stone seat on which it was more comfortable to sit than on the damp earth of the cemetery or the cold slabs on the graves. It was there that little Kamilla and I sealed our vow of eternal fidelity with that primitive seal, the kisses of adolescents. "Let me feel how your heart beats," I said, because I had read this phrase in a novel and it was followed by a row of significant dashes. The dashes in that book were no doubt meant to indicate more decisive happenings, but it would be difficult to relate by other means than dashes even the things that happened on that hidden seat at the time of our puberty.

We were not troubled by the hands which the tombstones of the high priests stretched out in a horrified warding-off gesture. The stones did not speak to us, nor did the bones under them, nor the divinity conjured with incomprehensible signs. We were alone.

On that day which I spent with little Kamilla it had rained outside and the rain was still in the cemetery, raindrops clutching at the bushes and shrubs to break the last stage of their fall when a breath of wind shook them down; then they died into the earth in front of the silver-gleaming tombstones. Puddles barred our way, the seat was damp and I sacrificed my handkerchief to dry it and my overcoat for Kamilla to sit on.

We paid no attention to the treetrunk standing two or three paces away, but began our kissing and I the exploration of her heartbeat; when Kamilla with a look of terror in her eyes, suddenly trembled. My eyes followed the direction of her glance and that was when I saw the neck, that obscene neck with the brown wrinkled skin, in a line with Kamilla's knee. The treetrunk was not a treetrunk but a man. He was standing and praying in front of a black stone sarcophagus on which the shallow relief of the square Hebrew script gleamed like molten tin. Now I, too, heard the litany he was murmuring almost soundlessly; he did not break off his prayers while he watched with outstretched neck the youthful trifling of a spooning couple and while his glance slid downwards over Kamilla's legs and then ran up again. Kamilla jumped up. I restrained her, for it seemed too silly to run away. I talked to her, forcedly and about trivial things and squinted at the man.

His white hair, in small curls, like wool, stuck out from

under his shabby flat velvet hat. Scarcely one-third of his
face was visible to me: a greedy pupil, the bulge of under-
eye pouches, the point of a prominent nose and the tousled,
untrimmed edge of a grey pointed beard on a tanned
cheek. The hand that swung with the rhythm of the
prayer was like buffalo leather. The man was very old,
but his body was not that of an old man. Black broad-
cloth breeches that shone with a tarry shine fitted tightly
on his thighs and were tucked into high boots. From
instep to crutch the legs seemed sinewy young legs of the
right proportions, only at the height of the hipbone did
they taper unnaturally into a too-narrow hip. The man
wore neither caftan nor overcoat, his black jacket was too
big for him, so big that even the rain did not succeed in
pressing it to his body. The width of the shoulders gave
the torso the shape of a triangle. From the left hand of
the old man, which I did not see, a leather sack dangled.
Kamilla and I wanted to wait until he had gone. But he
prayed on and on. So it was we who went away. Only
after we had gone twenty paces did we dare look back at
him from behind a stone: he was a tree-trunk again and
the dry brown branch pointed stiffly in our direction. I
saw his face. The lips moved in prayer.

After this, whenever Kamilla and I sat down somewhere
in the open air, she begged me with feigned playfulness:
"Look well whether that tree over there is really a tree."

Our little love affair passed and so did the years and I
was twice as old when I was once more reminded of the
meeting with the old man. It was the end of 1914 and the
Imperial and Royal Austrian regiment of infantry No. 11
was in winter quarters in Ofutak near Novisad. Defeated
by the Serbs and driven back over the Danube, we were to
be re-equipped, re-disciplined and trained for fresh deeds
of valour here. Every evening the officer on duty, before
making his rounds in the town to catch any soldiers out

without a pass after lights out, selected a few men on guard duty to accompany him. One day I was one of these men to go on the patrol.

On the outskirts, where the contour of the town melted away, stood the brothel. The officer ascertained from outside which of the windows were lighted, for in such a house all lights immediately go out every time a patrol of inspection enters it. That is well known to everyone who has been on this sort of duty before. This time only the right-side corner room had a light in it; the officer entered, paid no attention to the assurance of the madame that there were no soldiers in the house, knocked on the door of the right-side corner room and bawled: "Open up! Check-up!" A naked girl opened the door quite unconcernedly; the guest whom we had thus rudely disturbed was a civilian, a very ancient Jew. The officer took a look round the room, as though still searching for a hidden soldier. "How filthy that bed is," he said, just to say something.

"Well, I didn't lie in it," the old man protested, although the officer had not addressed himself to him.

"What are you doing here?" the officer shouted at him, but then realizing that this was fairly obvious, he continued:

"Are you a native of this town?"

"I am a pedlar, I have been coming here for many years, everybody knows me in Ofutak, I . . . ."

"Then see that you get home," the officer interrupted him, "there is a state of emergency, at ten everyone is supposed to be at home, as a matter of fact I ought to arrest you."

"Could I not stay a little longer?" begged the old man.

The officer laughed: "Didn't you say that you would not lie down it that filthy bed?"

"Please, sir, he never lies down in the bed when he is

with a girl," interposed the madame, lurking timidly behind us in the open door of the room. We left the house and continued on our rounds.

All that evening I tried to remember of whom that old man had reminded me; that tanned brown complexion, that head, that cheek and chin with the white negro wool sticking to it, that build resembling an hourglass, those strong sinewy legs in the enterprising riding-boots.

Not until next morning did it occur to me, that this brothel-visitor of the night before was the same as the treetrunk in the ghetto graveyard of my youth. Nonsense. What would a South Hungarian village pedlar have been doing in Prague and how could I have recognized him after so many years? Kamilla had been married a long time, she was a mother and the man who had eavesdropped on us had been a very old man even then; no, the praying visitor to the graveyard and the lecherous visitor to the brothel could not be identical, it was impossible! But I remembered the stiff neck and the glance which seemed to push up Kamilla's little frock, so fierce was it. Was not the same fierce greed in the eyes of the old man last night? Immediately after such an unpleasant interruption, having just escaped the danger of arrest, he had asked to be allowed to complete his love-making.

Had I met the old man in the streets of Ofutak, I would have spoken to him, but another ten years went by before I saw him again; this time again in the Jewish cemetery in Prague. When I first caught sight of him there I thought my eyes were playing me tricks. He was standing and praying in the identical spot where Kamilla and I had seen him stand and pray a generation before. I took a very good look at him this time and there was no doubt in my mind: it was the pedlar I had seen in Ofutak.

I walked past him as though by chance and spoke to him:

"I just wanted to tell you that the gate of the graveyard will be closed in a few minutes."

"I'll get out all right, the door leading to the house is left open," he answered, but nevertheless he ended his prayers, carefully selected a little stone from the sack which he carried in his hand and laid it on the three-hundred-year-old grave. "It is a stone from Jerusalem," he said, eyeing me keenly.

"This is the grave of Medigo del Kandia, isn't it?" I asked.

"How do you know that? Are you from the Chevra?"

No, I told him, I had nothing to do with the brothers of burial.

"Then how do you know whose grave this is?"

"Oh, I am just interested in the graveyard." As I saw that he was about to ask me another question about my connection with some religious institution, I added: "Only as a private hobby."

"Are you a doctor?" It seemed simpler merely to nod in the affirmative than to enlighten him as to my profession, which might possibly have made him suspicious or reticent.

"What do you know of Medigo del Kandia?" He asked the question, not like somebody testing another's knowledge, but more in surprise that a stranger should be informed of his private affairs: as though he had asked "how is it that you know about my dead?"

But this grave was one of the sights, I said, and the Cretan Medigo well known out of books, "He was, I think, a traveller, mathematician, astronomer, a pupil of Galilei, physician and a God-fearing man."

"Is that so? Do the books say so?" He seemed astonished.

"Yes. Is it not written here on the stone?"

"The things written on gravestones are nothing but lies."

"Then was Medigo not learned. Did he not travel a great deal?"

"Of course he was! Of course he travelled a lot. Perhaps more even than I . . . ."

"Or was he not a God-fearing man?"

"More so than all the others lying here. His piety was the real thing, Rabbi Jossef Shloyme ben Eliahu's."

"Why are you so surprised then that it should be written in the books?"

"Oh yes, afterwards they put it in the books. When a man is dead, they let him live."

"Who are 'they'?"

"Who? Men, of course! As long as one lives, one is hounded from place to place without peace and rest, and only when one is dead is one allowed to live. Believe me, young man, there is only one happiness in this world: to die. Then one is at rest and at peace, one gets a headstone and on it they write what one was, even though while one was alive, they persecuted one precisely because one was just that."

"But you just said, Mr. . . . . Mr. . . . . ."

"My name doesn't matter. What is it I just said?"

He waited calmly for my objection like someone who is sure not to involve himself in contradictions and who is able to extricate himself even if he had said something wrong. His manner was not that of a pedlar; his speech and vocabulary was that of a well-educated Rhinelander, only occasionally was the cadence oriental, as when he praised the blessings of death.

"But you said just now that the inscriptions on the headstones were lies."

"So they are! The graves lie with stone tongues! Read what is written here about Jossef Shloyme del Medigo!"

He ran his finger over the long flattened relief of the moss-covered runes and translated in illogically separated

groups of words, but fluently enough, the eulogy on the
stone:

". . . . and there was a great sound of mourning in all
Israel . . . ."

The grave was like a trim house that once had stood free
and had now sunk into the earth up to its gables and the
ridge of its roof.   As the old man bent over the house he
seemed tall, enormously tall. His hand read on the graven
epitaph:

"All God-fearing men honoured him . . . ."

Angrily he turned from the slab: "Who honoured him?
These here, who scratched into this stone here that they
are God-fearing? Bah! What they did was drive him out
of Vilno, out of Grodek, out of Hamburg, out of Amsterdam; the Karaites were against him because he defended
the Cabbala, the Rabbinic Jews were against him because
he was supposed to have spoken ill of the Sohar; in
Amsterdam they poisoned his life, in Frankfurt they treated
him like a galley-slave, everywhere he suffered poverty
and persecution—and afterwards they wrote on his tombstone ' . . . . there was a great sound of mourning in
Israel and all God-fearing men honoured him . . . .'
and all the rest of it."

"Perhaps he was better received in Prague?"

"In Prague? They drove him out of here, an old man of
sixty, four years before his death. He had to leave this
rich community on foot and he had a blister on his right
heel, this big . . . " (the old man rounded thumb and
index finger to show the size of the blister Medigo had
on his foot) " . . . and his sandals were torn. Fortunately
he found a Jewish cobbler near Eger, and the cobbler . . . "

What did the old man drag the cobbler in for? Did
he want to claim to be the man who had soled the shoes
of a wanderer three centuries ago?

He noticed my suspicion and corrected himself . . .

I

"some cobbler somewhere near Eger perhaps, a young man, much smaller than I, mended the soles of his sandals and the straps . . . ."

"But Medigo died in Prague and they gave him this fine memorial."

"Yes, he had to go to Prague once more and died here. And then they gave him a fine tombstone, on my word. And why? Because he was famous, this Rabbi Jossef Shloyme ben Eliahu, and because the Jews of Prague wanted to brag about the important people buried in their cemetery. Now the guides can tell visitors how honoured and how pious and how great all the dead were who lie here. And there are the same sort of things in the books too."

The old man jumped to the front slab of the memorial and bent down over the top, his fingers and eyes searching the concrete with which the ridge had been repaired.

". . . Rabbi of Hamburg . . . and in the environs of Amsterdam . . . *hafilosof elchi abor harofim*—a philosopher of the Divine among all sages—the strongest among physicians, astronomer and astrologer . . . his chief work *taalimis lechochmo*, the secrets of Wisdom . . ." He was about to read on.

"Is that all untrue then?"

The old man's brows contracted and he hissed:

"A truth hidden in a tangle of lies is a thousand times worse than a lie! It is a piece of meat in a trap. It is a torn shoe stuck together with cobbler's wax instead of properly mended. It is a book containing one saying of Solomon and in the rest preaching nothing but hypocrisy . . . I do not walk into a swamp even if the sun is reflected in it. I do not want any truth in a place which is full of lies."

He ran to a grave on which the tombstone stood black and aslant, overgrown with moss and furrowed with graven letters.

"Here you have another biography: 'and she was charitable to the poor and never missed a morning service . . . .'
But there is nothing on the stone about the goings on of
the pious Frummer while she was young and her father was
Jew-in-ordinary to Count Collalto. He was a merry
gentleman, was Count Collalto and with few prejudices.
Not many ghetto girls could boast of having been present
at a masque in the Collalto palace, eh, my little Frummer?
And then you married Jacob Budiner, he did well, the
ugly Jacob Budiner, to marry such a lovely wife, and
directly afterwards he became Jew-in-ordinary to Count
Collalto and later to Baron Popel. Baron Popel, too, was
a fine gentleman, wasn't he, little Frummer, and signed
a lot of bills and then you . . . ." He bent over the tombstone and went on ". . . and then you *bought a curtain
for the synagogue made of dark green silk with silver bells and
gold-embroidered lettering and studded with many precious stones'.*"
He sprang nimbly to another grave: "*Hersch Leibnitz. His
learning was great and the great lords listened to his words.* I
should say they did! They listened to him so much that
the Emperor Ferdinand gave orders for Rabbi Jontov
Lippmann Heller to be brought to Vienna in chains as a
sinner against the Emperor's majesty. For this Hersch
Leibnitz had falsely denounced him." The old man now
posed no longer, he was all hatred towards all those dead
ones, he jealously disputed the praise heaped on them,
so long turned to dust; shrilly he brought up the most
intimate private affairs in order to vilify the defunct; he
dragged the dead from the bowels of the earth and flung
them down again with a spiteful, mocking word.

He had just found a new victim:

"Here you can read; '*Here lies Josef Baroch, gold-and-silver-
smith, a man of strictly upright character.*' Strictly upright
character indeed! He bought some golden candlesticks from
a soldier, engraved with the initials E.W. and a coat of

arms. Later, when it became known that the candlesticks
had belonged to the governor, Baroch laid the candlesticks
down at the gate of the ghetto. The governor, Count
Ernst Waldstein had old Jacob Lämmel, head of the Jewish community, arrested and had a gallows set up outside
that gate by the haymarket, what is it called now, oh yes,
the New Gate, that was where Jacob Lämmel was to be
hanged if the receiver of the candlesticks was not found.
Joseph Baroch kept mum, this man of—what does that
tombstone say?—this man of strictly upright character.
He kept mum and the Jews could count themselves lucky
that the head of their community escaped being hanged
on condition that ten Jewish elders brought a fine of ten
thousand guldens in ten bags publicly to the town Hall.
And Count Waldstein used these ten thousand guldens
for a perpetual foundation to look after Jews who embraced
the Christian faith. But Josef Baroch lies, like any honest
man, in a marble sarcophagus engraved with blessings.
Such people may die . . . ."

"But did no one know that Baroch was the receiver?"

"Who would have dared to suspect him? Was he not a
man of strictly upright character?"

"But then how do you know it?"

He shrugged his shoulders and looked at me as though
he was afraid of having betrayed his identity.

"I am an old man and have travelled much. One gets
to know a lot of things that way—"

We went on. Of some graves he seemed to know
nothing. As we passed the small slabs on which a clumsily
engraved figure (more an ornament than an infringement
of the religious ban on effigies) showed that this was the
grave of a virgin, he made cynical remarks such as: "This
one might have been, at that, she was only ten years old
when she was lucky enough to die . . . ." or "When one
of them dies because she tried to get rid of an unborn

child, then she is a virgin." If the figure showed a rose
as a sign that the young woman buried there had been
engaged to be married, the old man laughed a bleating
laugh: "They call a bride '*nevesta*' in this part of the world,
that is derived from the Latin *vesta*." His wrinkly brown
neck grew stiff as it had that day long ago when he had
eavesdropped on my youthful loves. Reading a name he
hissed: "This one died of a nasty disease. He got it from a
French camp-follower . . . ." He scrutinized the epitaph.
"And with that he had eight children. Well, he probably
wanted to see what a Frenchwoman was like. Cost him a
pretty penny too—he had to give her three Rhenish guldens
or she wouldn't look at him and a year later he was dead,
on the very day when Marshal Belle-Isle marched out of
Prague."

Some graves he befouled merely by a contemptuous
gesture, in front of others he stopped, trying to remember
who it was that lay there and searching for clues on which
to base more blasphemies. Now and then he threw himself
flat on the ground with quite amazing agility, screwing up
his eyes to decipher some sentence; in this he did not always
succeed and sometimes his lips moved, as he read, without
making any spiteful comment.

For centuries now the Jewish cemetery in Prague has been
merely one of the sights, a jumble of legendary, mysterious
and buried things; but now I was walking beside a man
who pretended to hear the voice of the stones and to
maintain personal contacts with all past generations and
whose memory seemed to fill in the intervals of time. And
all his reminiscences were only defamation and abuse.

I waited with curiosity to hear what he would have to
say about the great Rabbi Löw, in front of whose little red
temple he stopped, pulled a wry mouth and nodded. He
put much irony into his voice as he read: ". . . '*Lift up
your voices in lamentation in weeping and mourning of the most*

atrocious pain, a howl of woe like hyenas, for a great prince in the camp is dead' . . . .   They are still howling like hyenas!" His index finger pointed to black spots on the stone slab, the traces of candles by the light of which Galician refugees of the great war had prayed all night at the grave of the miracle-working Rabbi for the safety of their lost families. "But it is in vain that they howl like hyenas! Why in vain? It says there on the stone: 'He ventured into the labyrinth of Pardes but he came out in good time and unharmed.' Aye, aye, at the right time and unharmed, so he did. That is why he cannot help anyone. And so all these *kvittels* here are no use—look how everything is full of them."

I peered through the chinks in the sarcophagus to which he pointed and saw hundreds of scraps of paper covered with Hebrew writing lying in heaps. "They help no one, these pleas," he repeated, "and dead Rabbi Löw helps no one, however much his epitaph praises him and however often I see the spot on the moon which is named after him. I won't throw any *kvittels* in here, not I."

On the ridge of many tombstones lay rows of pebbles, a sign of piety dating back to the time of Israel's wanderings in the wilderness. At that time, thousands of years ago great stones were rolled on to the graves of those who fell down dead in the desert, so that the vultures and jackals could not dig the dead bodies out of the sand; it was a pious duty of everyone coming after to extend the same protection from wild beasts to the dead buried there. This practical measure has survived as a custom and in the old cemetery of Prague many a pebble may have been placed on a grave in the Middle Ages and many others not longer ago than to-day. The grey-haired cynic at my side brutally swept away with his talk these mineral wreaths laid down by generations.

"These little stones lie just as much as the big ones. The

stones thrown at good men while they live, are put on the graves of evil men when they die. Those who are dead are pampered, but those who live are driven from place to place."

"But you, too, have put a pebble on a grave."

"Oh, *I* know whose grave I honour. I knew the men who lie here—that is—I mean—I know the story of their lives. But the others know only the fairy-tales the cemetery attendants tell. It costs nothing to lay down a pebble. These heaps of pebbles are only a plaything. Field Marshal Wallenstein was quite right."

"Who?"

"Field Marshal Wallenstein, the Duke. He wanted to consult Bath-Shevi, his Jewish Financier, ask him whether the Wallenstein thalers would depreciate if the army rose against the Emperor Ferdinand's majesty and how much Bath-Shevi would lend him for a campaign against the Emperor. But because the Duke's palace was full of spies, the Duke put on a Jewish gabardine and came to the ghetto by night. They had their talk on the grave of Hendel Bath-Shevi—Shmiles Bath-Shevi was accustomed to negotiating his business in the presence of his wife and as she had just died, he took the Duke to her grave. While they were talking, the Duke absent-mindedly took the pebbles from the grave and played with them. When Bath-Shevi saw this, he leapt at the Duke and gripped his hand. The Field Marshal started with fright and although Shmiles humbly begged his pardon for having dared to touch him—a Jew touch a prince, a Wallenstein!—the Duke trembled and could not say a word. He went away and never spoke to Bath-Shevi again."

Here I interrupted him: "But Wallenstein summoned Bath-Shevi to himself after this."

"After this talk? How can you know that? You knew nothing of this interview on Mistress Hendel's grave?

Then let me tell you that Prince Wallenstein never met Shmiles Bath-Shevi again."

"But Bath-Shevi died in the Duke's castle."

As though he had only just remembered it, the old man admitted that I was right. "When the trouble began about Bath-Shevi's dirty deals and he fled for his life, the Duke had to give him refuge near the Carthusian monastery at Jitschin. But whether he spoke to him there, I don't know, but they certainly did not meet again in Prague. Shmiles Bath-Shevi is buried outside, in Münchengrätz, although he ought to have been here among the men of Prague where all the rest are the same sort of . . . ."

He broke off. As though to make up for the untrue story he had just told me or as though he was sorry to have wasted time with the telling of the innocuous anecdote of the pebbles used as a plaything, he did not continue his orgy of defamation but took me by the arm and said:

"Come I'll show you something!"

I had already once before been surprised by the agility of the old man. Now I was surprised at the speed with which he approached his goal. Jumping across the Rabbi's Path he stopped on the patch of green, where the grass grows tall and rich along the wall giving on to the Salnitergasse, and with his foot pushed aside a dense network of ivy. A narrow stone now became visible, most of it sunk in the ground. "Announcement for coming generations," the old man read the first line aloud and asked me: "Do you know this grave?"

I had halted on the gravel path and looked at the grave which was the only one on that side of the path. Why did only such an unusually small part protrude from the mound? Why did it lie thus apart and why was it hidden under the ivy? I had never noticed it before, no guide had ever pointed it out to me, never had I found the slightest mention of it in any of the books describing the Jewish

cemetery of Prague, although the stone bore an "announcement for generations to come".

"You don't know it?"

"No, I have never seen it and never heard of it."

"Of course not. Take a good look at it: this is the one
epitaph that does not tell a lie!"

"What does it say?"

He bent down again over the Hebrew inscription; which,
when translated, read: "In the year 531 after the lesser
count (i.e. 5531 according to the Jewish calendar and
1770-71 A.D.)

Announcement for the coming generations: shortly after
this enclosed space was bought, as shown by the minute
book of the Chevra Kadisha, p. 5 . . . . with permission of
the august government . . . ." Under this line the mound
began. "One cannot read any further".

"Why not?"

His grin revealed a perfect row of very large teeth.
"Why cannot one read any further? Because the truth is
written there! That is the only reason! A dog is buried
there, a piece of carrion, as true as I live. There, under
the earth the inscription is hidden: 'Po nikberar n'velah—
carrion was buried there'."

"How did a dog get here?"

"How a real dog got here among so many dogs taken
for men, is that what you mean? Franzek Mrshak threw
him over here, who was the knacker's servant over the
way." The old man pointed towards the wall, "and he
did it to annoy the Jews."

Perhaps there was more to this drama in which the
knacker's man and the gravedigger were the actors, and
the stage the mystic scenery of the Jewish cemetery in
Prague and a secret grave. I tried to draw the old man out:
"This Franzek Mrshak must have been a spiteful fellow."

"That's as it may be. But I don't think he was spiteful.

He was a pious man; went to church every morning, to the Brothers of the Cross over there. And he cursed the Emperor Joseph for dissolving the monasteries—that was done at that time. He was not very clever, was Franzek, but he wasn't spiteful, although he had plenty of reason to be so. To catch mad dogs, collect dead cats and cart away dead horses is a nasty job. On weekdays he pulled his cap over his eyes and let his moustache droop so as to be able to change his appearance on Sundays. On Sundays he washed and groomed himself and turned up his moustache and went across the stone bridge . . . tell me, is that 'Kodosh, Kodosh, Kodosh' still there on the stone bridge?"

"Yes, the crucifix with the Jewish inscription is still there."

"I never set foot on the stone bridge. I prefer to cross by the ferry-boat."

"Why don't you cross by another bridge?"

"Now that there are other bridges, I sometimes do. But I will never go past that 'Kodosh, Kodosh, Kodosh' . . . . "

"Who was the Jew who was forced to pay for the inscription on the crucifix?"

"It wasn't a Jew at all. Count Pachta paid for it out of his own pocket."

"But the inscription says: 'Three times holy, holy, holy, erected with the fine paid by a Jew who had blasphemed the holy cross, by a worshipful Court of Appeal in the Autumn of 1754'."

"Yes, they engraved that there, a lie in stone, like so many others here in this graveyard. A Jew is glad if he is left alone."

"Why was it inscribed there?"

"In order to mock the One who really blasphemed, but that was very long ago, thousands of years ago and God himself punished the blasphemer."

I brought the conversation back to the knacker's man.
"Where did Franzek Mrshak go on Sundays all washed
and dressed in his best?"

"To an inn near the Sand Gate where there was a dance,
I can't remember the name of the inn. Franzek was there
every Sunday, but no one knew who he was. His girl's
name was Pepcha—in those days nearly all girls were
called Josephine and all boys Joseph—and some of the
boys got jealous. They found it suspicious that Franzek
would never tell even Pepcha what his trade was and
where he lived. So they followed him one day and saw
him go into the knacker's yard. When Franzek came into
the dance hall next Sunday and was about to ask Pepcha
for a dance someone shouted: 'Franzek Mrshak, look out!
Here's a nice little job for you!' and with that a dead dog
came hurtling into the hall, a putrid piece of carrion, all
green and bloated, with the teeth bared and the worms
wriggling in the mangy coat. Poor Franzek wanted to
vanish, but they didn't let him, he had to take the
dead dog and carry it through the town, in his Sunday
best, straight from the dance, mocked and for ever separated from his Pepcha. As he was running along with the
dog, a pedlar was coming along the street, Pinkas Street
it was, and the two collided. 'Can't you look out, you
filthy Jew?" yelled Franzek and swung a blow at the Jew
with the dead dog. The Jew ran away and then Franzek
Mrshak thought to himself that there were some human
beings held in greater contempt than even a knacker's
man. 'But they deserved it,' he thought to himself, 'one
of them mocked our God as he went to his death. Let
them do the dirty jobs. This Jewish huckster nearly
knocked me off my feet! And what a fuss they make with
their cemetery, their land reaches right up to our wall now.
Why don't they take our whole knacker's yard too and
have done with it? I, a Catholic Christian, am not allowed

in the dance hall and must not dance with Pepcha, but the Jews who have mocked Our Lord on His last road may spread themselves all over the place. Well then, let these mockers of Our Saviour bury the dead dog, I make them a gift of it for their new cemetery section.' And that is why Franzek Mrshak threw the dog over the wall to the Jews."

"And why did the Jews bury the dog here?"

"What could they do? Throw it back? Then there would have been a tremendous fuss, that the Jews are throwing carrion over the wall of their cemetery. Or were they to call the knacker to the graveyard? The brothers of the burial just buried the dog in the still unused part of the cemetery." He crushed the ivy underfoot. "Of course they hide this grave! Why? Cannot a dog be good and true? Why do they degrade it after it is dead? Why do they throw it into a dance hall and are ashamed of its grave?"

The old man bent forward and prayed. Then he pulled a pebble out of his pedlar's pack and laid it gently on the sharp edge of the grave slab. "Perhaps the dog was still quite a puppy and God in his mercy let him die young."

We walked towards the exit and out into the street where we met a Mr. Lieben, who gave my companion a hostile look and did not return his mumbled greeting.

"That was Jonas Lieben, wasn't it?" I asked the old man who was obviously displeased by the fact that I knew Mr. Lieben.

"Mr. Lieben is known as a pious man," I remarked, but my companion said nothing. "Is he not pious?" I asked again, being curious to know whether the old man was as hostile to living Jews as he was to the dead. "Other people are pious too," he muttered. "That makes no difference, does it?" I put in.

At that he burst out: "A man is not pious if he does not

leave other men in peace, if he thinks that he has a monopoly of piety. People who don't belong to his set count for
nothing, or else they are cheats and swindlers in his eyes."

We were crossing the open space in front on the Rudol-
phinum, a tramcar went past, courting couples were sitting on the seats along the embankment but otherwise
there were few people about.

"I am taken short," said the old man. "Do you think I
could squat down here?"

"Come a little further along, I'll show you a public
lavatory."

"I never use a toilet. I never sit down." He was already
unbuckling his belt and squatting down.

For the first time in two hours I was alone for a moment.
I was standing in front of the Museum for Applied Art;
there was a telephone kiosk there with a notice on its glass
door: "Insert one crown or two fifty heller pieces." Above
me on the bastion a few windows were lighted. A gully-lid
in the pavement looked like a check-pattern patch on
grey cloth.

What was the old man after? Why did he play the part
of Ahasuerus for my benefit? "I never sit down" was the
last thing he had said just now. Rather clumsy. But had
not the brothel madame in Southern Hungary, that time
nine years ago, confirmed unasked that he never lay down
in the bed when he came to one of her girls?

For hours now the old fellow had been telling me stories
centuries old, stories no one could check. No grandchild
of these dead was still alive, no great-grandchild, no one
who might know anything else about them than the things
to be found in books or on tombstones. Still, it was strange
that he had been praying at a grave when he thought himself unobserved, and prayed long, and that it was the
same grave at which I had seen him pray a quarter of a
century ago. Even then he had been very, very old. I

had not heard anything of little Kamilla for many years, her children must by now be far older than she was at that time.

The old man was squatting there in the open street like a street urchin. He could be seen from the windows.

Why did he speak ill of Mr. Lieben? Did he want to forestall any adverse opinion of himself that Mr. Lieben might express? Mr. Lieben had not returned his greeting. That could be due to the fact that all strangers out so late are suspect.

According to the legend, Ahasuerus mocked Him as He was dragging His cross along and drove Him from the threshold of his house—that would be quite in character so far as my companion was concerned, who would even drag the dead out of their graves to heap insults on their heads.

By now the old man had joined me again. He appeared to be disposed now to return to realities. He asked me whether I was a native of Prague? What was my name? Of Zderas Street?

"No," I said, "my people live in Melantrich Street."

He did not know this street. I described it to him. "Oh, you mean Sulphur Street." He knew only the old name. But he knew Zderas Street, a corner in the new town, of evil repute and the Kischs he knew were precisely the ones who kept a house of ill fame there.

I asked what he dealt in. "Cameos," he said.

"Cut stones?"

"No, written ones. Holy cameos as protection against evil."

"Amulets, you mean."

"Well, we call them cameos. I'll show you one."

He leaned against the parapet of the embankment and groped in his pack. A courting couple was walking slowly towards the Academy building. He waited until they had gone. Then he unrolled a small hexagonal piece of parchment covered with Hebrew words of five letters each, placed under and over each other; a silk thread was looped through the point of the hexagon.

"This cameo is very old and well-tried, it will protect from trouble and disease. It costs a hundred crowns."

"I'll see how much I have on me."

The eyes of this old man who roamed the world like one burdened with an eternal evil, and, oh irony! sold lucky charms, stole towards my wallet.

"Buy the piece, it will bring you luck. As for me, I am an old man who cannot live and cannot die, cannot sit and cannot lie. As truly as I hope to die: I envy that dead dog I was telling you about."

We walked on. I was to wear the "cameo" round my neck, he advised, but take it off on Friday evening and not put it on again until after sunset on Saturday, for on the Sabbath one should wear nothing except one's clothes. Did I know any rich people, especially women, who were interested in miracles and prophecies, in the wisdom of numbers, in the Cabbala? "I can explain much and calculate much in advance that is to come and I have a perpetually shining skull as a shield against anything untoward."

I told him to come to my house the next day. The strains of a gramophone reached our ears from a restaurant. The old man stopped in front of the window: "That is jazz music, I like to hear that, it turns the saddest tunes into merry ones." As we got to the Stefanik Bridge he took his leave, saying: "Tomorrow I will come to your house for certain." After I had gone a few paces, I turned round, curious to see in which direction the old man had gone, but he was nowhere to be seen.

I went to Mr. Lieben and asked him who the old man was. "That old man. A rogue, that's what he is. His name is Issachar Mannheimer and he is a native of Worms. Had trouble with the police in Prague before this, once he bought candlesticks from Prussian soldiers, although that was strictly forbidden. The candlesticks were marked with the initials W.E. and he knew perfectly well that they belonged to the governor."

"Count Ernst Waldstein?"

"Whatever put Waldstein into your head? Nothing of the sort. The governor was Weber-Ebenhof, in 1866."

"But in that case this Mannheimer must be very old to-day."

"Very, very old. He was no longer a youth even in 1866. The whole Jewish community suffered because of that affair. The head of the Jewish community was arrested as a hostage and the elders of the community had to pay a fine. Mannheimer will not stay long in Prague, now that he knows I have seen him here."

"He knows an amazing lot."

"He talks a lot and lies even more. Among the Jews in the provinces he claims to be a messenger of the Chief Rabbinate of Palestine, and among Christians—you will laugh—he tries to pass himself off for the Wandering Jew. He disgraces the Jews in the whole world. What did he want with you?"

"Oh, he only explained the cemetery to me."

"I can imagine the sort of explanations he gave you! Nothing but lies, I dare say!"

"Is it true, Mr. Lieben, that a dead dog is buried at the foot of the cemetery wall?"

"So he took care to show you that particular grave! Just like him!"

The old man never paid me his promised visit.

CHAPTER TWELVE

The Ties of Death are Strong

O N E day you might find yourself far from the Lower East Side, on one of the Jewish cemeteries on Long Island, "Mount Hebron" or "Montefiore" or one of the others. They are not like one of the old Jewish cemeteries of the old world, not like the one Ruysdael painted and Goethe described, nor like the famous one of Prague. Here are no primeval thickets of bushes and square tombstones stooping like old men.

But you would find something that would appear strange to you: these cemeteries are divided into sections by fences and hedges, that is to say they are made up of different groups of graves. Here, you might reflect, the same sort of distinctions seem to operate as over there among the living on the Lower East Side. And that is how it is.

Death and even the prospect of death makes it difficult or impossible for the melting-pot America to amalgamate the Jews with each other, much less with the surrounding world. A Jew can live in any conditions, but he wants to be buried among his own people. This was the main reason why Jews from the same places of origin first formed associations.

Once in New York a poor man was buried in the Greek-orthodox cemetery, although he was of the Jewish-orthodox faith. His co-religionists and countrymen wanted to transfer the dead man to his rightful place. But exhumation is expensive, they had to collect funds, borrow money and guarantee repayment on a co-operative basis and that was how the first association of countrymen was formed in 1859. Others followed and the waves of immigrants which were beginning to reach the shores of the United States, broke, so to speak, on a familiar beach.

Naturally this was merely the obvious, visible beginning. As there had been Jews here before the date indicated, there had also been welfare organizations and cemeteries. The first Jew on North American soil was for a long time the only one. He had landed on 8th July, 1654, from the Dutch ship *Preboom* at what was then New Amsterdam. His name was Jacob Bersimson and he searched right and left for a homely Semitic profile. But nowhere could he find a co-religionist to guide him to a kosher table or to a group of ten Jews, entitled by this their number to hold divine service. He searched in vain both in the Wall-straat (now Wall Street) and in its social antipodes, the Bowery—he could find no other Jew except himself.

Every morning Jacob Bersimson went down to the land-ing-stage and mustered the new arrivals. Alas, no one! To make sure, he afterwards posted himself under a tree and began to wind on his phylacteries. Perhaps, he thought, perhaps someone will go past one day and recognize me as a brother by this rite.

And so it was! One day a dialogue took place, the exact words of which will be willingly communicated to you by one of the partners to it, if ever you meet him. This man, already quite incredibly old, even in Jacob Bersimson's day, a man of sinewy build, with a giant beard, strode up to the praying Bersimson and told him, but without stopping—all the time he was speaking, he walked without a pause around the tree under which Bersimson was pray-ing, he too, without a pause—that he should not despair because of his loneliness. At the next new moon so many Jews would arrive in New Amsterdam that Jacob Bersim-son would be able to dine at the table of a different family every day of the month and would have the choice of three groups of ten for his prayers. Then the restless stranger strode out of his circular movement at a tangent and disappeared.

The thirty families which landed at the next new moon from the three-master *Sante Catalina* were Portuguese Jews of Dutch nationality, coming from Brazilian territory. They had gone there from Rotterdam at the time the West Indian Maatschappij had conquered Brazil in 1624. But now that the Dutch had been driven out, the Jews had to go too, and they arrived in Manhattan in order to keep the Jewish Robinson Crusoe, Jacob Bersimson, company.

The Jews increased in numbers, built the first synagogue and laid out the first graveyard. But unfortunately nothing has come down to us that might throw light on the history of the famous families Spinoza, Akiba, Acosta, Disraeli, Balsamo, Bizet, etc. Even the grave of Lorenzo Daponte, who wrote the words for those two masterpieces of music, "Figaro's Wedding" and "Don Juan", and who died not more than about a hundred years ago, was sought in vain by a frenzied reporter of our time on what remains of the cemetery in Oliver Street.

The cemeteries have had to give way before the on-slaught of the sky-scraping real-estate prices which split the rocky soil of Manhattan into little pieces. They fled ever farther north, but the real-estate business followed them relentlessly and only on Long Island did the cemeter-ies find peace for the time being. Perhaps it is a more durable peace, for the organizations which cared for the graves are not merely religious but also regional bodies.

Each of the three to four thousand such organizations, known as countrymen's associations, unite one hundred and fifty members. Membership is voluntarily compulsory, so to speak; each group has its own prayer-house, its own religious school, its own welfare institutions and above all its own burial brotherhood.

The geographic place of origin in Europe often no longer exists. In both world wars many Polish, Russian, Ukrainian,

Bessarabian, Rumanian, Galician, West-Prussian, East Prussian, Slovak, Carpatho-Russian, Lithuanian, Latvian and Esthonian localities were broken out of this globe together with their Jewish communities. But the Jewish communities, destroyed and exterminated in Europe, live on in the United States. In that other world this side of the ocean they quietly carry on with the life of the old *Kehille*, full of a local patriotism which lacks a locality and all reason for patriotism. Even while the old home locality existed, it had not been a very friendly one and often enough the Jews had been beaten, violated, robbed and killed.

This side of the ocean the family feuds of the old home are carefully maintained and the piety or wealth of long-dead ancestors still carries weight. It is as though these long-dead ancestors might enter at any moment and intervene in the affairs of their posterity. And all this in the most un-mystic place in the universe, New York!

The cement that holds the countrymen's associations together is death; death, being much more durable than life, is also the more important. This point of view is found in the oldest documents, for instance those relating to the case of a certain Baruch Berger. One day a Mrs. Berger of Freehold, a little town in New Jersey, wrote to her countrymen's association, informing them that her husband had died and that she needed the sum of fifty dollars to prevent his being thrown into a pauper's grave. The countrymen's association immediately dispatched a delegation to Freehold to bring back the body. But they found that the dead man was alive. Baruch Berger had contracted debts, was threatened with arrest, infamy and death by starvation and had therefore decided to have recourse to this last resort. But a claim which would have been legitimate after death turns into fraud when it is made in order to escape from death.

According to this logic a dead pauper has the right to far more than the five to ten dollars which is the maximum he would be accorded as a living pauper. For a dead man all the cost of dying is paid, he need not pay rent for his last dwelling and defray removal expenses. That does not mean, of course, that in an earthly world in which inequality is a basic principle, men are treated in an equalitarian spirit after death.

There are certain private undertakings (at least they call themselves "undertakers") who make a living out of dying—the dying of other people, of course. These other people they strive to attract with special allurements. Like all American "morticians", the Jewish undertakers give their dead female clients a beauty treatment with hair-do and make-up. They advertise that they provide a silver hearse for those entrusted to their care, that they supply a little bag with authentic hallowed Palestine soil to put under the heads of the dead or that they will erect an extra-special tombstone "designed by the most famous sculptors of Paris".

Various private insurance companies inform the general public by means of posters that their entire membership is bound by the rules of the organization "to go out to *Beth Chajim* with the *Levaya* of a *Balboth* of the organization" the reader of such posters is not intended to consider the trouble of having to attend the *Levaya* (funeral) in the *Beth Chajim* (literally "house of life", actually cemetery) of every *Balboth* (member) of the same organization; he is supposed to think only of the advantage to himself of being the subject of corporative attention on the occasion of his own *Levaya*. . . . Many organizations possess a banner, many others a band as well and all have speakers practised in graveside oratory. It goes without saying that provision is made for a temple singer to be present, the temple singer representing for many Jews the only available music in life as in death—opera and concert in one.

But what no undertaker, no friendly society and not even the synagogue can supply, is the homeland. The homeland, the associates from the same land of origin can be provided by the countrymen's associations alone and these they do provide for the dying fellow-countryman and for the dead one, at the bedside, at the graveside and at the memorial rites. Therefore everyone must look ahead betimes and accord all honours due to the burial section of his countryman's association. Thus in this section such countrymen as are not distinguished either by eloquence, religious learning, social success, dignity of comportment or a charitable hand may often also win esteem.

The rights and privileges of the brothers of the burial are laid down in the rules of the countrymen's associations. Every year on the 15th of the month of Kislev a banquet must be held in their honour; on this occasion they also elect their Chairman and Vice-chairman "of which the first-named must be able to read and write, at least in Yiddish". On the eighth day of the *Succoth* week as well as on the last day of the Passover week and on the second day of *Shevuoth* the members of the *Chevra Kadisha* have the exclusive privilege of reading the week's section of the *Torah* in the synagogue.

When someone dies, the brotherhood of the burial informs the examiner who issues the death certificate, the newspapers who will publish the announcement of death and the obituary, the rabbi attached to the countrymen's association, and the guardian of the cemetery section belonging to it, where a grave-digger, also a countryman, immediately begins work on the grave.

The graves are far from the Lower East Side, but the rooms in which the dead man's countrymen commemorate him in prayer, are quite near; all around Second Avenue there are more than a hundred prayer houses. The furniture consists of the Ark of Covenant, with a table for an altar in front of it and a baker's dozen unpolished deal chairs. Not even forms are required, as the association hires a hall for the great feasts or else its members secure seats for themselves in the big synagogues. But for the ordinary everyday worship the ten chairs suffice for the *Minyan*, that minimum number required for prayer, at one time so painfully missed by the Jewish Robinson Crusoe of Manhattan. But the particular ten who are to speak the prayer for the dead man's soul twice every day through the year of his death, are not to be utter strangers but if possible, co-nationals from the home country.

There are pious men who come to pray every day in any case; there are also others who practise the trade of a *Minyan-man* for a consideration and these are the poorest among the countrymen. If the one or the other man of the *Minyan* is missing, a man must be borrowed from a neighbouring prayer house if they have a man to spare to make up another *Minyan*. But an amalgamation of the countrymen's associations beyond such co-operation would be regarded as betrayal of the home country, as treason towards the anti-semitic, pogrom-making nest in Europe which is the country of origin. This separatism is the community spirit of the foreign quarter, which one might call the Disunited States of Europe within the United States.

But do not forget that the Lower East Side is merely one side, as indicated by its name, or more correctly only a part of one side. In the Upper West Side and all the other sides of the city and all over the territory of the States there are far more Jews than those living on the Lower East Side. The army of grandsons and great-grandsons includes every sort and condition of citizen, all types and characters, all trades and professions, all degrees of wealth and fortune and every shade of opinion. Forgotten often enough are the origins, the transit stage of the Lower East Side and the countrymen's association, sometimes even the Jewish faith itself. But unforgettable is the desire to be united after death with kith and kin, friends and countrymen.

CHAPTER THIRTEEN

The Golem

I

THE little Jew with the excessively high forehead lived in a lean-to adjoining the wooden synagogue in Wola-Michowa. It was in this corner of the Carpathians that our company found itself in 1915, after having been pulled back out of the front line to act as reserve. The barrage thundered into and out of Wola-Michowa day and night; the village street spouted up, sheaves of fire spurted heavenwards, houses collapsed even if not hit, every second brought a clap of thunder crossed by another burst of sound. But the little Jew with the excessively high forehead remained in his wooden hut with his wife and his eleven-year-old son. He had partitioned off a corner from the rest of the room with two tarpaulin squares and that was where he slept. The rest of the hut was a billet. Yesterday for Russians, to-day for Austrians, to-morrow for Germans. The little Jew didn't care.

Behind the stove lay a confused heap of books. The officers and soldiers starved for something to read, had often picked them up, but they were all Hebrew print and so they were thrown back even quicker than they had been taken out, to occupy their place in the heap behind the stove. I may have turned the pages of one of the books a little longer and the question of the little Jew: "You can read that?" led to a conversation.

When I told him that I was a native of Prague, he looked up in surprise and now it was I who wanted to know whether he knew my native city. "Of course I know Prague!" he boasted with a sort of sly pride, but when I asked him when he had been there he answered: "Never in my life."

"Then why do you say you know the place?"

"I know it from the books."

From the confusion behind the stove he fished out an old guide to Prague. "I know it from books, perhaps I know more about Prague than many a native of Prague."

"Why are you so interested in Prague of all places."

"I want to go there one day. Prague is a fine city and has a pious *Kehille*." Then he added cautiously: "But perhaps I will go somewhere else after all."

He told me later that what interested him in Prague above all was the grave of the great Rabbi Löw and the place where the Golem lay, the figure of clay which the great Rabbi had once formed and endowed with life.

"Where does the Golem lie then?" I asked.

He made excuses—he didn't know exactly where, but he was sure he would find it if he were in Prague.

That evening I took up the guide and turned its pages. On the map of the city I found pencil marks connecting the old synagogue with two neighbouring alleys and leading from there through the new town out to the edge of the map.

The next time I spoke to the little Jew I mentioned that I had once heard that the Golem lay in the old synagogue. The little Jew shook his head in negation.

"I know why you think that," he said. "You know this book here, don't you?"

No, I did not know the dark leather binding which he picked out of the chaos of folios with unerring certainty and began to read to me.

The preface quoted an expert opinion by Dr. A. Berliner lecturer at the Berlin training academy for rabbis, to the effect that the book was a hotchpotch of superstition and ought to be burned, not published. The publisher countered this crushing criticism by saying: "It is those who do not believe in proven facts who should be burnt, not this book."—

The little Jew with the excessively high forehead was entirely in agreement with the publisher, he had no doubts whatever as to the truth of the data given in the book, but thought them incomplete. For had he not a continuation of it, a manuscript chronicle, which he did not mention to me until we had become fast friends and I had promised him by everything sacred that I would not begin to search for the clay image until he, the little Jew, had joined me in Prague.

Then he solemnly brought out his treasure, a manuscript of sixteen octavo sheets covered with Hebrew writing. He told me he had it from a wise man whom he had met in Prezmysl and who had charged him only eighty guldens for it. The price did not appear excessive to my friend in Wola-Michowa—for him the papers contained all the secrets of existence. When he smoothed the pages, he seemed to caress them. But the printed, leather-bound volume he gave me as a parting gift when I left.

II

Translated, the title of the book reads: "Strange Tales in which are described the Miracles of the great world-famed Master-mind, by name Maharal Miprag—blessed be the memory of that pious and holy man—which he accomplished with the Aid of the Golem. In Hebrew and Yiddish, published by Hirsch Steinmetz in Frisztak, printed by E. Salat in Lemberg in the year 5671."

The book tells for what reason and in what way, after an interview in the Hradcany palace between the Emperor Rudolph II and the High Rabbi Löw, the latter withdrew from the Golem the vital force he had bestowed on it.

That the Emperor Rudolf II had received Rabbi Löw in

audience is a historic fact. On Sunday, 23rd February, 1592, Prince Berthier transmitted to Mordechai Meisel and Isaac Weisl, elders of the Jewish community, a command of the Emperor that Rabbi Löw should come to the palace. Obeying this command, the Rabbi went to the Hradcany, accompanied by his brother, Rabbi Sinai, and his son-in-law, Jacob Katz. Prince Berthier conducted Rabbi Löw alone into another apartment and there questioned him about the Cabbala. He spoke in a very loud voice, in order that the Emperor, who was standing behind a curtain, might overhear the conversation. Suddenly the curtains parted, the Emperor came forth, addressed a few questions relating to the subject of the conversation to Rabbi Löw and then retired behind the curtain again.

There can be no doubt that Rudolf of Habsburg, dabbler in astrology and alchemy, wanted to find out something about the secrets of the Cabbala. That Rabbi Löw, the High One, was versed in it was well known and he himself admitted as much. "Those who understand these my sayings, know also how deeply rooted they are in the wisdom of the Cabbala," Rabbi Löw wrote in a polemic, and in another tract he began a passage with the words: "If one knows the Cabbala, the teachings of which are the truth . . . ."

The audience described in the book of my friend in Wola-Michowa preceded the authenticated historical interview by two years. The Rabbi allegedly obtained from the Emperor the concession, that no one would henceforth be permitted to accuse the Jews of ritual murder and that the street in which the Jews lived would in future be protected from violence. (In the soon following Easter days of the year 1590 the usual Easter excesses against the ghetto did not in fact take place.)

After the audience the Rabbi Löw—still according to

the book—summoned his son-in-law, Jacob Katz and his disciple, Jacob Sosson, the Levite, and announced to them that the Golem was no longer required and was to be eliminated. Jossile Golem himself is told by the Rabbi that that night he was not to sleep in the judgment room, as usual, but in the attic of the old synagogue.

It is *Lagb'omer*, the thirty-third of the forty-nine days counted between Easter and Whitsun. At midnight the three men climb up to the attic. During the ascent Jacob Katz begins an argument about whether he as a Cohen is permitted to go near to a dead body; Rabbi Löw enlightens him that the life of a clay doll formed by a human hand was not life in the divine sense and its death no death.

III

But it is not a simple matter to deprive the Golem of its artificial life, if we are to believe our book. Rabbi Löw, Jacob Sosson and Jacob Katz take up their positions at the head of the sleeping Golem, just as, at the time when Rabbi Löw breathed life into the clay figure, they had stood at its feet. Their eyes directed towards the feet, they walk seven times round the body, muttering in a sing-song their mysterious formulas. At the seventh round, the Golem's life has been turned into death; what is left lying there is a lump of earth dressed in human clothes, mere dumb clay.

Rabbi Löw summons Abraham Chajim, the temple attendant, takes from his hands the two candles he has brought and places them at the feet of the now lifeless figure, which he then undresses, the discarded clothes he wraps in prayer-shawls. Eight hands take a good grip and push the clay colossus under a mountain of books and papers heaped up here, so that not an inch of it remains visible. The clothes are taken downstairs and burned.

Next day the rumour is put out that Jossile Golem has

had a brainstorm and has escaped in the night. A week later Rabbi Löw decrees that henceforward no one may set foot in the attic of the synagogue, and books and documents may no longer be kept there owing to the danger of fire. "But a few shrewd men," the book concludes, "knew that the Maharal Miprag issued his ban only in order that the Golem lying up there may not be found."

At this passage the little Jew of Wola-Michowa with the excessively high forehead had always shaken his head with a superior air, for was it not written in his expensive manuscript what had afterwards happened to the Golem? He smiled at the "shrewd men" who had thought the burial in the attic to have been the definite end of the Golem.

IV

When I saw the little Jew with the excessively high forehead once again, he was no longer smiling. It was two and a half years later, in Vienna, in the Leopoldstadt. His curly hair had grown grey and had thinned, the high forehead was all furrows and wrinkles. He stopped me with a tired gesture when I began to speak of the Golem: "I have other things to think about," he said. A shell had torn his son to pieces in the lean-to of the temple in Wola-Michowa and shortly afterwards something terrible had happened to his wife, he did not say what it had been. "She is in hospital and I have no money." I took him to an inn, but he ate almost nothing. We found we could not get a conversation going, for our common memories were tied up with a village in the Carpathians which he wanted to keep out of his thoughts.

"So you don't want to go to Prague any more?" I asked him. "All that no longer interests me," he said. "In that case may I search for the Golem?" "Please yourself. You can have the manuscript too, if you like."

He brought me the manuscript in the afternoon and put the price in his pocket without counting the money.

V

In Prague I tried to get hold of the key to the attic in the old synagogue, but failed. All I got was a refusal. I was told that no stairs led up to the attic inside the synagogue. The attic could be reached only by climbing up the fire-escape on the outside wall and that would attract too much attention. Ever since a chimney-sweep, in the seventies of the last century, had fallen from the roof and remained lying dead in the road with a shattered skull, no one had been up there. Before the great fire in the Vienna Burg-theater there had not even been that fire escape; it was installed in 1880 by orders of the fire-police.

I obtained permission from the synagogue authorities to climb up to the synagogue roof. I arrived one morning at eight o'clock. Mr. Zwicker, who for thirty-eight years had been the honest guardian of the building, warned me once more not to go. To my question whether he had ever been up there himself, he returned the counter-question: "did I think he was *meshuggah*?" Then with a shrug of his shoulders and a "Have it your own way," he obeyed the orders of the authorities and handed me the key.

I climbed over the railings which surround the bare little garden of the temple, pulled my wooden ladder over after me and propped it against the wall under the iron rungs of the fire-escape. The lowest of these is six feet up from the ground, to prevent unauthorized persons from climbing up. With the eyes of astonished passers-by fixed on my back, I climbed first my own wooden ladder and then the eighteen iron rungs, swung myself up into the Gothic-arch-crowned recess and opened the groaning iron door.

I entered a room shaped like a steep pyramid. Only hesitatingly did I venture to advance, for the floor was not even, it ran up and down in irregular bumps. These corresponded to the Gothic arches which undulate in stone waves in the prayer hall under my feet and above the head of worshippers. Up here they dovetailed into each other in rough unplastered zig-zags. I seemed to be walking on a chalk hill, but walking less on my feet than with my hands with which I groped forward and which either slipped off or dipped deep into thick layers of dust. My face was brushing against cobwebs all the time.

An iron transom ran across the room. On the floor lay an old stovepipe and the skeleton of a bird which had died here in lonely agony. Fungus grew rankly everywhere, in all sorts of grotesque shapes. A bat hung head downwards between the beams.

In the hollows between the sharply meeting arches the rubble had conglomerated into a solid mass through the action of lime dust and moisture. If the Golem was buried under it, he could not be exhumed except with a pickaxe.

Truly a place as well suited to the mystical experiments of Rabbi Löw as to those of the Paris canon Claude Frollo; a meet sleeping place indeed for a dull monster, whether its name be Quasimodo or Golem. As a matter of fact Victor Hugo's *Notre-Dame de Paris* is nothing more than the Golem legend lifted from the squalor of the Prague Ghetto into the celestial neighbourhood of the Paris cathedral-towers. King Louis XI, seeks advice from the mystagogue Canon Frollo, as Rudolf II seeks the counsel of the Rabbi well versed in the Cabbala. Esmeralda inspires love in the hunchback Quasimodo, as the Rabbi's comely grand-daughter in the Golem of the Prague legend. A mob bent on violence attacks the Ghetto of Prague as the inhabitants of the Paris "Cour des Miracles" of evil repute storm the Cathedral.

The bat is beginning to swing to and fro in alarming fashion. If bats awake they entangle themselves in human hair. No sign of the Golem.

I get back into the open-air, half-close the creaking door behind my back and set my foot on the uppermost of the iron rungs. Then I shut and lock the door and climb down. Meanwhile a little crowd has gathered in the street.

In the anteroom of the synagogue I wash my hands in the old copper basin. "Well? Have you found him, the Golem?" inquires Mr. Zwicker in a tone which combines curiosity with pleasure at my failure.

VI

Thus the climbing expedition to the roof of the old synagogue did not lead me to a meeting with the Golem. This fact alone would have confirmed in the eyes of my friend from Wola-Michowa that the data in the dark leather-bound volume were out of date, and his own manuscript up to the minute.

"You can take my word for it, he wasn't up there any more when the Maharal forbade anyone to go up there. Abraham Chayim, the *shammas* and his brother-in-law had taken him away . . . . ." he had said to me in Wola-Michowa.

My poor friend from Wola-Michowa! There was nothing in your precious manuscript to warn you that a shell would tear your child to pieces and that your wife would be raped. There was nothing in it about other things either: that you would lose your faith in miracles and driven from your homeland, would tramp the streets of Vienna in despair. How indifferent you had grown to the Golem by the time I inquired about him from you in Vienna. In 1915, in Wola-Michowa, you explained to me, proud of your knowledge, the very road the dead

L

Golem had taken. You wanted to follow the same road to recover and revive the servant possessed of superhuman strength, just as Abraham Chayim the *shammas* had tried to do four hundred years before you.

Immediately after the rite of taking off the spell had been completed, that temple attendant, Abraham Chayim, had conceived the desire to use the Master's discarded automaton for his own ends. He communicated this plan to his brother-in-law and fellow-*shammas* from the nearby Pinkas synagogue, Abraham ben Secharya his son-in-law Asher Balbierer, who studied the Cabbala, was to find out how the Golem could be awakened to life again. A few days later Asher Balbierer announced that he had found the proper incantation in the Zohar. In the dead of night the three men lifted the Golem from the grave in the pile of old documents in the synagogue attic and carried him away to a cellar in the house of Asher Balbierer.

There they began the resuscitation. They took up the same position that Abraham Chayim had seen the rabbis take up; they walked seven times round the Golem, from feet to head, muttering ceaselessly the formula "discovered in the Zohar" by Asher Balbierer. In fact it was probably a quotation from the Pentateuch about the creation of Adam: "and blew a living breath into his nose and thereupon he became a living soul."

But it was all no good. The lump of clay lay like a lump of clay, defying all attempts at resuscitation, never batting an eyelid. Asher Balbierer pretended to be surprised: "That's what I call being dead!"

At this time there was an outbreak of the plague in Prague and two hundred people had already died of it, say the chronicles. Asher Balbierer's two elder children were in bed with a fever. His wife, Mistress Gele, had already objected to receiving the Golem into the house, fearing that should it be discovered there, her father, her husband and her uncle would all be punished for disregarding the rabbinical ban. In addition she presumably had little confidence in the Cabbalistic arts of her husband. When the children fell ill, Mistress Gele was convinced that it was the Golem who had brought bad luck to the house and when both children died, she demanded insistently that the Golem should go.

After the dead bodies of the children had been washed and placed in their coffins in the presence of the funeral guests, one of them was secretly taken out again and put in the same coffin as the other child. The second coffin was used to accommodate the Golem. At sunrise a cart carried the two coffins with the three bodies to the plague-pit outside the gates. Abraham Chayim and Abraham ben Secharya carried the coffin with the Golem up Gallows Hill "the which lay one mile and two hundred fathoms outside the New Town Gate, on the Vienna road", and there they buried him "on the side looking towards the city of Prague, on the evening of the Fifth of Adar".

VII

The meaning of the Golem legend—the desire for power and the overcoming of this desire—is raised to the second power in this manuscript tale: the magician who copies the creation of Adam is followed by his servant who, being a servant, desires in his turn to have a servant. Like the master high up in the roofbeams, so the sorcerer's apprentice low down in the basement struggles with the lump of clay. The Master himself destroys his sacrilegious creation. The Apprentice is hampered by superstition in his superstitious attempt at resuscitation—he mistakes the stone guest in the cellar for the killer Death, lugs the clay away in terror and buries it in unhallowed ground.

The strange thing about the manuscript is that all its data referring to times and places coincide with historical fact. Even Abraham ben Secharya, the temple attendant of the Pinkas synagogue is a real person; his tombstone in the old graveyard tells us that he died in 1602, having held his office for thirty years, i.e. during the time to which the manuscript refers.

The description of the road from Asher Balbierer's house to the burial-place of the Golem is in accordance with a contemporary map of Prague "Praga Bohemiae Metropolis accuratissime expresse 1562"; two and a half kilometres from the battlements we see on this map, Gallows Hill, marked with wheel and gibbet.

Out there in the Zizkov suburb, on a low sandstone hill, poor sinners were done to death for many centuries. The last of them, a young waiter who had murdered his pregnant sweetheart, was carried out there in the hangman's cart on 18th June, 1866. Ten thousand people watched the execution from scaffoldings and the surrounding hills; ballad-singers, showmen and pedlars were busy all that day, the day which was the day before the battle of Königgrätz with its columns of wounded, with its message of death and destruction, with the crowning shame of Bismarck's entry into Prague.

The thunder of guns at Königgrätz in 1866 .... It was while guns thundered in the Carpathians in 1915, that my friend had explained to me why he had drawn a pencil line on the map of Prague towards that hill on which I have just set foot, following in the twentieth century a trail laid in the occultist era of Rudolf II.

VIII

Here I am on the spot to which the Golem is said to have gone on his last journey. It is a scarcely fifteen foot high ridge with scattered tufts of grass here and there.

Evening is coming on. The sirens of the factories have hooted their last. The roofs of the cemetery chapels nearby loosen their outlines. Over the chimney of the cartridge factory a column of light-grey stiff smoke stands motionless. An athlete is running round the cinder track of the Victoria Sports Club. A sentry stands very bored, in front of the house which is the seat of the Committee for Small-Arms Inspection. The huts in the allotments look like earth-closets of peasant cottages. Couples are searching for the least-exposed dips in the ground. Children, rickety, ten to twelve years old, stalk the courting couples like Red Indians in order to learn something about the facts of life.

The hills are honeycombed by the digging of men who have come here for sand. In each hole there might be a coffin, and in it the Golem, covered with sand.

A little girl, perhaps three years old, has brought out a tin chamber-pot and starts making sand pies in it. The mother who is sitting there with a soldier, pushes the pot away with her foot and beats the wailing child; the mother's lover looks on and laughs.

Men and women, stooping and weary, are returning from the factories to homes where another spell of work awaits them.

At the graveside of the Golem I understand why the robot unconditionally subject to the will of another, must be buried deep and irretrievably.

CHAPTER FOURTEEN

Leather   Trade

o l d Velemin is sitting in an empty second-class compartment. His eyes are closed, but he is not sleeping for all that, not even dozing.

"Grandpa," Eric asked him once, "why do you always shut your eyes?"

"I am playing chess, my boy."

"Where are the chessmen you are playing with, Grandpa?"

"The chessmen? I get them out of my memory. In my memory there are heaps of pawns, and knights, and bishops, and I use those to play with."

"Grandpa, why aren't all chessmen alike, like the pieces in halma or draughts?"

"That is just what chess is like. The chessmen are different from each other and they move in different ways."

"And do you know in advance what moves they will make, Grandpa? Even the pawns?"

"It is the pawns who start the game, my child. It is a long time since I first started as a pawn."

"But if you know every move, you must win every time, mustn't you, Grandpa?"

"People say that I am a good combination player."

Eric did not understand at the time what a combination player is.   Now Eric is a student in Annonay, at the leather university. Will he learn there how to be a good combination player?

"Leather University?" old Velemin smiled ironically. In the old days one did not send one's boys even to the polytechnic, but now it must be a leather university, and in France at that.

My own leather university I entered when I was eight

years old. I tramped from village to village buying rabbit skins for Cejka, the dealer who sold them to the hat factory at Oberwalden. I paid the peasants four kreutzers for each skin, sometimes as much as five, and I, myself, got six from Cejka, the dealer. My profit was fifteen kreutzers a day per saldo, and I dreamed of a great future. When the Emperor Francis Joseph dies—why shouldn't I be emperor then? And once I am emperor, I shall be even more than just emperor, because I will earn money on top of being an emperor. I'll roll cigarettes by night for the tobacco monopoly and in the daytime I will deal in skins. Cejka the dealer, will pay me at least one kreutzer more if I am emperor . . . .

Well, I did not get to be emperor, only an Imperial Councillor. I did not want the order of St. Leopold, because it is called the Order of the Leopold quarter (Leopoldstadt, the Jewish quarter of Vienna. Tr.) Anyway people poke fun at me in the trade when I go to the Café Fetzer or the Café Danube. That is where the leather dealers sit playing Buki-Domino, and when I come in they shout at me: "What shall I play, Mr. Imperial Councillor? May it please you to give me your imperial counsel." But afterwards they come to me to get business advice "because you are our genius in combination." Since when have I had that reputation? Let me see . . . .

I still remember the first of my "combinations". We bunny-hunters—that was our nick-name with the children who did not have to go out and earn money—we bunny-hunters knew that the first skin of the day was the hardest to buy. The farmers' wives—the farmers themselves were mostly away working on the land—either told us that there were no skins in the house or demanded six kreutzers apiece, a price we could not pay. We boys thought that was as it should be, because the proverb says that every beginning is difficult. But in the long run I was not

satisfied with this state of affairs and I racked my brains
to find out why every beginning should be so difficult.
The farmers' wives probably think, when we arrive without skins, that the other farmers must have thought our
price of four kreutzers too little. Or, perhaps, when they
see that we carry no skins in our hands, that there is a
scarcity of rabbit-skins and that the price would go up.
The more persistently we tried to persuade them, the more
stubborn they grew.

From the day onwards, on which I had thought all this
out, I always took a few skins with me from home when I
started out—as a "first purchase" so to speak. In the
morning they were quite light to carry, but in the evening
they weighed heavier than the others, those skins I had to
cart along all day without any profit.

As I walked across the fields the thought passed through
my mind: what sort of a man can this Cejka be? He was
amiable enough with us bunny-hunters. When one of us
entered his shop, Cejka directly patted him on the back
like an old friend, and made jokes. He also gave us acid-
drops, all sticking together. We bunny-hunters liked him
well enough because of all this, but I was puzzled by a
contradiction. If Mr. Cejka was as fond of children, as he
always told us he was, why then did he beat his own? The
Cejka children often went about all bloody or with ban-
daged heads. Was he deceiving us when he joked with us
and, if he was deceiving us, why did he do it?

Sometimes he tried to deduct a kreutzer from our money
because a skin was cut or otherwise not perfect. He had no
money, he always said, he was a very poor man. Much
later in the course of my life I have often met business men
who complained that business was bad and that they had
no money—by doing so they wanted to make people believe that they were rich and thereby improve their credit.
But as a child I did not understand that a man may tell

the truth in order to tell a lie, I did not sense the wisdom
of the saying: "Don't make yourself so small, you are not
as big as all that." Yet I felt instinctively that Cjeka the
trader was diddling us.

I was pretty anxious to find out how much he made out
of our rabbit skins. So one day I set out to go to the hat
factory in Oberwalden. I lost a full day's earnings by this
trip—it took me more than half a day before I could get to
see the stockkeeper, because even then I was as small as I
am to-day.

The stock-keeper told me that he paid a gulden for two
pounds of rabbit skins. I was no wiser than before, because although I had carried many a rabbit skin on my
back, I had never weighed them. But now I saved up all
my rabbit-skins and when I had fifty of them, I took them
to the mill to have them weighed. But I need not have
taken so many at all, ten to eleven skins made two pounds.
From that day onwards I sold no more skins to Cejka, the
dealer, but made my mother sell straight to the hat factory
not only all the skins I myself collected in the villages, I
also bought the skins from the other boys, paying them
two kreutzers more than Cejka did, and myself earning
twice as much.

Now I bought myself a pushcart and started buying
cowhides, pig-hides and even horse-hides. There was
scarcely a knacker's yard between Pisek and Budejovice,
where I had not been. Often they sold me rotten hides
which had long lain in the knacker's yard.

The skins the hat factory did not want I sold to a man
called Kozeluh; he was tall and lean and had a tannery
down by the Votava river. He gave me a good price, but
he paid slowly and later not at all. But I still brought him
the skins and spent many an evening with him. He had
once been an army lieutenant in Dalmatia and Italy, and
had many stories to tell, especially about women. I did

not quite understand his yarns, but I could still repeat them to this day, they made such an impression on me.

That is not surprising; Kozeluh himself could not get his woman-stories out of his head either. When he got any money into his hands, he immediately went to Bude-jovice and blew it all to the last farthing.

I often went out to buy things for him, lime, tallow, paraffin, stearine and tar for shammy leather. He did not always pay me for my pains, just put it down to my credit, in his accounts. Soon I saw that he wanted to fail in business because he wanted to be rid of his tannery. And one day he was gone.

When the bankruptcy proceedings were opened, I turned out to be the chief creditor, and I was allotted the whole business. Five years later the rich Mr. Sinaiberger in Eibenschütz offered me thirty thousand crowns for the tannery. He had taught his son the saying: "Sinaiberger, never be a tanner", but he himself bought all the tanneries he could lay his hands on. And so did his son after him. I did not sell my place; although I did not want to be a manufacturer, but only a leather dealer, I had no inten-tion of giving up my little bridge-head in the industry.

That I took over the "Seven League" boot and shoe factory in Münchengraetz was something I had not in-tended to do. One day the owner came to me, a fine gentleman he was, a baron too, and showed me an order for forty thousand pairs of boots for the Serbian army. Could I supply him with leather for soles and uppers on long-term credit?

Why did he not go to the man who had supplied him before? And why did he need a long-term credit if he had an army contract in his pocket? I'll think it over, I said, and asked him where I could let him have the answer. He said he was staying at the Hotel Sacher and would stop in Vienna to the end of the month.

The Hotel Sacher is where Archdukes and noblemen go and the money he would spend there would have paid for the leather going into at least eight hundred or eight hundred and fifty of the forty thousand pairs of military boots. "I'll tell you what, Mr. Lazanski," I said, after a while, "why should I think this deal over such a long time? I'll let you have the leather on a two-year credit." I knew perfectly well what he was thinking when I said that. He thought: "This Velemin thinks I can be given credit because I am staying in the Hotel Sacher, that impresses him."

I supplied him until I came to be the chairman of the creditor's meeting and most of the estate fell to me. Then the "Seven League" boots marched on. With my son and my two sons-in-law, I turned myself into a joint stock company and now I am chairman. After a few years I moved away from Vienna and now when I go there I never set foot in the office, there is a lot I don't like there, and they can manage well enough without me.

Of course sometimes old Velemin comes in quite useful. This last September, for instance, they probably wondered a bit again at my "genius for combinations". I called up my son-in-law one morning bright and early: "I just wanted to tell you that you are not to take up any preference shares of the Vienna Financing Bank."

"What do you mean? Why do you think that we had any intention of doing so, papa?"

"Well, didn't you take over a parcel of the bank's shares after the 'Baden Trunks and Bags Ltd.' went bust?"

"How did you know that?"

"Because the Vienna Financing Bank was the backer behind 'Baden Trunks'."

"And why do you think that they are now offering us preferential shares?"

"Well, if they could not hold a business like 'Baden

Trunks' then the bank is wobbling. And if it is wobbling, then it must find new financial backing, new large shareholders."

"And why should they pick on us?"

"Because you've already got a parcel of their shares. So it appears logical and simple that they should offer you the young shares first and at a specially low price."

"Quite true, papa. But so it is logical and advantageous for us."

"Disadvantageous, you mean. They want to jockey you into holding a majority of the shares, in order that you should become responsible willy-nilly, if matters go wrong."

"But we have no intention of taking over a large parcel. Others can take over much more, especially on the stock exchange."

"Believe me, they won't offer any shares to anyone else. How many are they offering you?"

"One thousand shares."

"Have you taken them?"

"We decided to take them yesterday, but the letter has not been posted yet."

"Good. Tell the others that I am exercising my veto. Shall I put that in writing?"

"Quite unnecessary, papa. I'll ring up the members of the board immediately and tell them about your objection. At bottom I agree with you. I think you have again done honour to your famous gift of combination."

Old Velemin smiled into his beard. "That was three months ago. Yesterday I read that the Vienna Financing Bank was 'restricting the sphere of its operations'—a new word for going broke." And old Velemin in one corner of the compartment asks himself whether Eric will learn such things at the leather university in Annonay.

In Veseli-Mezimosti a young man gets in. He has light

reddish hair. He opens his case so that the half-open eyes of old Velemin can see a few shirts wrapped in tissue-paper, straight from the draper's shop. The young man takes a brief-case out of the suitcase and a "Neue Freie Presse" out of the briefcase and sits down, not without hitching up his trousers to save the crease. Everything he is wearing is brand new, the suit, the tie and all. The shoes (made by "Seven Leagues", old Velemin notes with satisfaction) are scarcely worn and the suitcase (made by the late "Baden Trunks") has not yet made a round-the-world trip either.

So rapidly does the young man go through the newspaper that each page is given scarcely a second of time. Only in the middle of the paper, where the official notices and law reports are usually to be found and where the financial and economic news begin, does he definitely settle down to his reading by smoothing back the pages along the edge with his thumbnail. Then he begins to read.

Old Velemin shuts his eyes completely now. This railway line is the oldest in Austria, or rather a continuation of the oldest railway line in Europe, the one between Linz and Budejovice. Old Velemin recalls that many years ago he had read aloud to his mother, read all about the Dreyfus case from the newspaper. When he came to the name Zola, his mother cried: "That is surely the son of Mr. Zola, the engineer who built our railway, he too, was a very, very kind gentleman." Now the railway runs all the way to Brno and in Veseli-Mezimosti there is a junction with the Vienna-Prague-Berlin express.

That the reddish young man who got in at Veseli-Mezimosti comes from Vienna can be seen at a glance. That he is a lawyer is also obvious. A doctor, for instance, would certainly not start his perusal of the "Neue Freie Presse" by reading the official announcements or the economic columns. A business man might do that, but business men generally don't wear horn-rimmed spectacles and don't carry brief-cases.

The purpose of the young Viennese lawyer's journey is also quite obvious to old Velemin. If he were travelling to a court hearing or to confer with a client, he would not be taking half-a-dozen shirts with him and would not be fitted out with new things like this. That is done only when a man is courting.

But whom? Old Velemin considers the geography of the line, or to be more exact, of half the line. For if the goal of the journey lay in the eastern half of the line, the young man would not have travelled by way of Veseli-Mezimosti, but by the shorter way straight from Vienna to Brno. Hence only the bit up to Jihlava need be considered.

The next station is Hradec. He cannot be going there, or he would already be preparing to get out. Then come the stops Jaborschitz, Tremle, Polichka and Dranovice. But in none of these do any families live who might aspire to having a lawyer from Vienna come to marry their daughter.

What about Teltsch? That is more probable. There is first of all the Weingarten glove factory. In the trade old Weingarten had been called the zoological Weingarten because he had a complete menagerie in his factory. He experimented with all sorts of animals to find out how they could be educated while still alive to make good gloves. Kangaroos jumped about in the grounds. Seals swam about in the dyeing vats, lizards crawled right into the office and chamois climbed the stacked boxes in the store-room as though they were rocks. The whole trade laughed itself sick. Let them laugh themselves sick, said Weingarten, and he meant it literally.

Now it is his son-in-law, Werfel, who is in charge of the factory, the son of "Kohn & Werfel" in Vienna. I can

recall the wedding of young Werfel and Miss Weingarten
as if it had been yesterday—it was a very sad wedding
indeed.

I was travelling to the wedding in the same train as to-
day—old Velemin thinks on. In Veseli-Mezimosti somebody got in and sat down opposite me. And it was my old
friend Kohnstein of "Kohnstein & Werfel", the one with
the fair hair, like shammy leather.

I told him he was looking well, like a young man.
Kohnstein protested, said it was only his hair, it never
changed; but he said he didn't feel at all well, travelling
up and down the country was getting too much for him.
But he said he had to go to Teltsch because his partner's
son was getting married. His own son should have gone,
but his son's wife was having a baby, and so, said Aaron
Kohnstein "I had to go". After that he said nothing more
and I thought he was thinking of his death. After a while
he said, as if to console himself: "Well, perhaps I shall be
a grandfather to-morrow." But the next day he was dead.
He had a stroke right in the middle of the wedding dinner.

That must have been just about thirty years ago and the
girl whose hand this young Viennese lawyer will ask in
marriage to-morrow is a daughter of young Werfel, that
is obvious. Before young Werfel got married and went to
Teltsch he had been a bit of a rake. He had spent most of
his nights in a bar with young Kohnstein, with my son
and a few more of those "bloods", the "leather princes".
Now they are all married and have children of marriage-
able age. . . .

What an ass I am! How is it that I did not think of that
before? Where are my eyes, when they are closed? Of
course, that's how it is! The young man sitting opposite
to me, just where the shammy-blonde Kohnstein sat on
his last journey, is his grandson, that is evident.

Of course his name would no longer be Kohnstein. A

full-fledged Viennese lawyer, if you please, cannot remain Kohnstein. But what can be his name? According to the latest regulations only two letters of the name may be changed. Perhaps the name is Kolmstein now. No, that doesn't sound well, four consonants bunched together. Kollstein? No, "l"-s are out of fashion now, the stock exchange pokes fun at all the Kohns who are now Kohls and Kolls and Kolms. He is much more likely to have chosen an "r". "Kornstein" for instance. No, that would be mixed up with Kohnstein too easily. "Korrstein" is less suspect. "Korrstein" "Korrstein?" Just a moment! Haven't I read recently that a Dr. Arnold Korrstein has been appointed legal adviser to the Leather Manufacturers' Association? I remember wondering who that might be."

Old Velemin opens his eyes and addresses the young man sitting opposite: "Excuse me, aren't you Dr. Arnold Korrstein? Of Vienna?"

The young man can only gasp "Yes", so amazed is he.

"And you are travelling to pay a visit to the Werfel family in Teltsch, aren't you?"

The young man is even more amazed than before. He is overwhelmed. "How could you know that?"

Old Velemin answers with a smile, "Just one of my combinations."

Thereupon Dr. Korrstein recovers his presence of mind and says to his fellow-passenger: "Then permit me to do a bit of combination too: you are old Mr. Velemin."

CHAPTER FIFTEEN

Emigrants in Amsterdam

FROM the gable of the Antoniuskerk Christ stretches out his arm towards the people on the Waterloo-Plein below. "Ladies and gentlemen" he might be saying, "come to me. I stock all the goods you bought up to now from the firm of Moses & Aaron, but my house is better furnished than that of your present suppliers."

The two witnesses by his side are two bearded, Jewish-looking, larger-than-life priestly figures and might very well pass for Moses and Aaron, even though they may in fact be Peter and Paul. At all events they stand there and raise no hand to protest against the claim, made in golden Gothic script, that the two religions are identical:*"Quae fuit a saeclis sud signo Moysis et Aaronis, stat salvatori renovata illustrior aedes."* Below this appeal those to whom it is addressed, the ghetto-dwellers of Amsterdam, hold their market and no one has ears to hear what the figure up there is saying in stony patience, no one has eyes to see the inscription on the church wall.

Even more beseechingly than the Christ up there, the Jewish stallholders stretch out their arms and their appeal is even more eulogistic and insistent than His. Passers-by are fully occupied with examining the goods offered for sale; pretending to disapprove of the goods, they ask the price of the selected object, bargain, go away and return again. A dealer who is gutting herrings and cutting up cucumbers, acts as though he was surrounded by a crowd eager to buy, a crowd pointing at him in awe, a crowd timidly whispering his name and against which he must now defend himself:

"Yes" he yells in stentorian tones, "yes, I am *the* Heimann, everybody knows that! Heimann is known to everybody! I am *so* well known!"

If real customers approach and Heimann has to get down to bargaining, his wife takes over the job of proclaiming his fame. She wears a "sheitel"—a euphemism for a wig—makes a trumpet out of her hands and informs the world that Heimann is *so* well known!

"Alles om een Dubbeltje" thunders a neighbouring Stentor; with a sweeping movement of his bunched fingers he folds a packet of notepaper, adds a propelling pencil, a watch-chain that looks like gold and a lollipop to all the things one can get for a Dubbeltje. "Nuttige Kadoches" are praised by another vendor and that is not supposed to be Berlinese, or Yiddish, but Dutch and French and to mean "useful presents".

Vegetables and eggs and fruit, "kosher plant margarine" fish and poultry and meat, all "under rabbinaal toezicht" are bought and sold in the swirling eddies of trade on the L-shaped Waterloo Plein; rusty ironmongery, threadbare clothing, broken furniture, battered crockery, pots and pans, Verkoop van 2ᵉ Handsch Gereedschappen en bruikbare Materialen—all the rubbish of the Netherlands is marketable ware here.

So it goes from dawn to dusk on every weekday on Waterloo Plein, on Sundays, fair-like, on the Oude Schans and the Uilenburgstraat. Only the Sabbath brings peace and quiet. On Friday afternoon Israel folds its tents, the posts, tarpaulins, boxes and unsold goods are either taken away in handcarts, in which raven-locked thin boys serve as cartdogs or are removed by water. Zwanenburgwal, "Wall of the Swan's Castle", thus poetic is the name of the quay alongside of which are moored barges full of old clothes and gondolas full of bicycle parts (for Amsterdam is the city of the Jews and cyclists and still had nothing to do with the first world war). A lurching canal-boat full of stark naked, defective window display dolls draws whoops from the idlers along the canals because of the obscene interlacing of the figures.

If a trader has only a small stock, the residue of which can be quickly packed and taken away in a suitcase, he usually stays behind on Waterloo Plein, for now that the competition has gone, he hopes to do some business. Late quotations, reduced prices, sales, special offers, remainders, Koopjes, Mezijes. Heimann is still there, but the crowd is still absent, that crowd whose rush he pretends to be beating off as he yells: "Yes, yes, Heimann is known to all!"

In the middle of Waterloo-Plein is a space surrounded by wire netting: a playground for the children, who play here during market-time and afterwards, while their poorer contemporaries push away carts or scavenge among the rubbish left behind on the pavement. Heimann's shouts "I am *so* well known", swelling to a finale, can be heard here, but it cannot possibly be his self-praise alone which fills this typical city playground, bedded deep in the bustle of the market-place, with waves of evil smells.

For the smallest children there are sand-boxes for making sand-pies, for the bigger ones there are swings, for those bigger still gymnastic apparatus. The biggest of all are playing netball; both teams consist of boys and girls, the girls in short skirts. The pace is fast, the skill considerable and the shoppers, loaded with their purchases, stop at the wire netting to watch, a prey to spectators' fever.

Even when the church clock strikes, no one looks up—much less does anyone raise eyes to the Christ who indefatigably stretches out His arms towards those who might be willing to admit that His Church is only what has stood under the sign of Moses and Aaron for centuries and has now been creatively renewed in a more glorious edifice.

God knows there have been plenty of attempts to convert the Amsterdam Jews before they were Jews of Amsterdam. In Poland and Russia they were approached with far more potent arguments, with robbery, rape and pogroms; in Spain and Portugal it had been dungeon, rack and stake, but it had all been no use, no use at all.

The Cathedral of Toledo—truly a more powerfully alluring, a more powerfully confusing, and a more powerfully intimidating edifice than this Church of St. Anthony—has stood ever since in a street in which no Jew can be found—but that did not protect the street from one day being re-christened Calle Carlos Marx; the street sign with that name was fastened, of all places, on the palace inhabited by Torquemada in his day and later occupied by those who succeeded him as Archbishops of Toledo. The alabaster-lined synagogues of Toledo were turned into Catholic churches, but the banished pew-holders built themselves other synagogues on the opposite side of the European map. Not far from Waterloo-Plein there are two of them facing each other. The "High-German Synagogue", was founded by Jews who fled from the landsknechts and marauders of the Thirty Years' War and from the Khmelnitzky's soldiery. The other is the Portuguese synagogue. The Portuguese synagogue is not at all like the Old-New-Shool in Prague; it is by no means a rickety, furtive gathering-place of outlaws—it is a splendid edifice, a Jewish cathedral. It stands in the middle of the river, on piles, or if we are to believe the rumour, on barrels of pure gold. The nave lifts heavenwards on pillars of round sculptured granite, like those of the Iberian churches to which the Jews were dragged for enforced baptism or to listen to sermons intended to convert them. The altar-rails are of Brazilian palisander-wood. The altar, or "Tuba", stands in the centre of the house; the concentric rows of seats face it and each other and not the east, as in the temples of the West, where the worshippers see only the back of the leader in prayer. Here the worshippers turn towards the east only when the *Torah* roll is taken out of the Ark of Covenant. One of these rolls comes from the old homeland—the fugitives carried it with them over the Pyrenees, like a banner after a lost battle.

Six hundred and thirteen candles give light for the divine service—an expensive and obsolete method of lighting, quite true, but that cannot be helped; thus it was in Granada, thus it was in Lisbon, thus it must remain. As in Granada and Lisbon, the Rabbi here wears breeches, silk stockings and buckled shoes, the officers of the community sport the flat, stiff Jesuit hat with curled brim and, the temple attendants have retained the fulminant three-cornered hat worn in Spain by the Guardia Real then and the Guardia Civil now. The choirmaster who directs the singing of the orphan boys has a velvet cap on his head like that worn by the scholars at Saragossa.

A marble tablet bears, in the Portuguese language, the names of the community elders during whose time of office the synagogue was built: "Parnassimos Senhores Ishac Levy Ximenes, Mosseh Curiel, Abraham Jessurun d'Epinoza, Danile de Pinto, Ysrael Pareira, Joseph de Azveldo, Zagachi Gabay Aboab de Fonzara, Semuel Vaz, Osorio da Vega and Henriquez Costino se estron est esnoga construida...." Worshippers greet each other with "Boa entrada do Sabbath"; across the road, among the "High Dutch" the formula is "Gut Schabbes" and instead of "Boa Semane" they on the other side of the road only wish each other a "Gut Woch'". The prayer for the Queen of the Netherlands is spoken in Portuguese and care is taken that certain formulas of the community documents are couched in the language of those who had tormented and driven out the ancestors of the now living.

Costume, demeanour and customs of those are preserved, who had stoned the Jews first in Spain and then, in the first emigration, in Portugal.

There in the south they had been called marrano, i.e. pigs, because they had publicly forsworn their faith at the behest of the Inquisition but had in secret continued to practise it. In the new home they now wanted to show that no caballero could outdo them in dignity, that no grandee could bear himself with more grandezza than they.

The Dutch provinces of the Spanish crown, the Protestant Dutch fought against the Catholic usurpers, and the victims of intolerance and of the Inquisition met with an all the more hospitable reception among the enemies of their tormentors, as they had not come with empty hands from their stepmother-country, but brought with them, in addition to the *Torah* scrolls, a well-developed trade with the Levant and South America. In the merchant citadel on the Amstel there was no "Juderia", no ghetto shut off by walls or chains; any man whose credit was good exercised the same civic rights and had the same freedom to practise his religion—provided it was not the Catholic faith. Only once, at the beginning of their stay, were they—who in Iberia had been accused of holding Jewish services under the guise of Catholic prayer-meetings—raided in Amsterdam during worship—they were suspected of being secret Catholics!

The Jewish caballeros strutted about in Amsterdam, they had riches and titles, their tombstones and even the cases of their prayer-shawls were decorated with coats-of-arms. In the museum rooms of the old City Scales one may see circumcision knives of agate with scabbards of walrus-skin, spice boxes of ivory, bonnets of Brabant lace for the Madrinie, (the mother of the bride) and for the Padrinie (the mother of the bridegroom), embroideries in pearls, temple utensils studded with precious stones and golden Easter vessels. The emigrants wished to be regarded as important, rich and noble, and no lesser man than Goethe had confirmed that they were that, although he had never seen the Portuguese Jewish community, may not even have heard of it and did not know to whom he was giving his testimonial. In his essay "Jacob van Ruysdael as Poet" Goethe describes a landscape; it shows the cemetery at Oudekerk of the Portuguese Jews of Amsterdam, a circumstance of which Goethe was ignorant. "Remarkable and strange graves of all sorts, partly reminding one of coffins in their shape, partly marked by great stone slabs standing upright, furnish proof of the importance of the parish and of the wealth and nobility of the generations resting here."

That cemetery is still there and although tram No. 8 runs straight to it, it is still wild and romantic and its faithful likeness might easily pass for a product of the poet's imagination. Those who lie under the oldest monuments are grandees like Samuel Palache, envoy of Sultan Mulay Sidan of Morocco, Mozes Jehuda Beori, *embaxador* of Mohammed IV at the court of King Charles IX of Sweden, Manuel Teixera resident of Queen Christine of Sweden to the Hansa; founders of the diamond cutting trade and famous jewellers like Manuel Baron Belmonte, Curiel and Duarte del Piaz; merchants who sailed to and fro between Brazil and the Netherlands, bringing coffee, tobacco, olive oil and much else. On the tombstones one reads names and insignia of physicians, pupils of the Moorish healers, like Joseph Bueno, who was called to the deathbed of Prince Maurits, and his son, the physician Ephraim, called Bonus; Gomez de Sossa, physician-in-ordinary to Cardinal Infant Ferdinand, stadt-holder in the Netherlands; authors of travel books, translators of Lope de Vega and Cervantes, divines and philosophers lie buried here, among them Doctor Semuel da Silna who with his *Tratado da Immortalidada de alma*, published anno criacao do mundo 5383 (1623 A.D.) had ideologically prepared the way for the excommunication of Uriel da Costa. Uriel da Costa could not bear the shame of the anathema, he recanted and then, ashamed of his weakness, took his own life. Traces of how the emigrants vied with the monks of Spain in bigotry, intolerance and mysticism we can find in the old prints of the library of the community, the Livraria Montezinos, one of the low houses that surround the synagogue like a fortress wall. Don Silva Roza, the librarian, does not like to show his treasures, least of all those dating back to the end of the seventeenth and the beginning of the eighteenth century, the days of Sabbathai Zevi, who called himself the Messiah. No community in all Jewry adhered to him with such unconditional fervour as the Spaniol community in Amsterdam. It hoped that this God would now lead them back to the Promised Land along the same road they had come: first to the Iberian Peninsula and after that—but to this they obviously attached little importance—to Jerusalem. The first stage once reached, in Castile, Aragon or Portugal, the homecomers would be full-fledged grandees of Spain, with swords at their hips and the Order of the Golden Fleece on their breasts, Hallelujah!

The Jews are doomed to be rootless, a people of nomads. And yet they longed for centuries to return to a home country which did not want them, they longed for a mighty kingdom, the gold-laced nobles and the elaborate ceremonial, even at a time when all the royal power and pomp and nobility was long gone with the wind.

The Eastern Jews across the road had, of course, never felt such longings; the return to the lands of the Tsar had no attractions for them, they remained suspicious of the upstart Messiah, disputed his vocation, spoke slightingly of him. The Sephardim cried out against such sacrilege and adhered even more fanatically to Sabbathai Zevi; the men of priestly blood were made to bless the community every Sabbath as a sign that heaven on earth had come (this is still done to this day) and the old prayer-books which Don Silva Roza shows us, although none too readily, have strange copperplate frontispieces which show Sabbathai Zevi enthroned above the clouds, a crown upon his head, rays of light emanating from him, and angels blowing trumpets all round him, announcing: "You are the Eternal, our God, Sabbathai Zevi!"

"A swindler, that's what he is," came back from the other side of Jonas-Daniel-Meijer Square. "A vulgar cheat!" and a civil war of religion raged through the Amsterdam ghetto.

If the Montezino Library proves the interest the Sephardim took in literature, science and theology, if the building of the synagogue shows their architectural ambitions, the contents of the glass cases in the old City Scales their love of craftsmanship and the sepulchral monuments at Oudekerk their appreciation of sculpture, one must seek a fifth locality in order to ascertain their attitude to painting and draughtsmanship: a ghetto house in the middle of the Jodenbreestraat. It was here that Rembrandt van Rijn had lived from 1639 to 1657, almost the sole Germanic inhabitant in a neighbourhood of Mediterranean and Eastern Jews. (Like him, long before him and far from him, El Greco had settled down in the core of the *Juderia* of Toledo in order to be close to the restless old-testament types, even though these were already beginning to ensconce themselves behind the New Testament.)

The Rembrandt house swarmed with Jews and it is still swarming with them to-day; the great master of the house is dead, but his models are alive. The precepts of the religion of Moses forbid the adherents of that religion to make for themselves images of what is up in the skies and down on earth, and of course also to cause others to make such images for them. But the soul of the emigrants was full of their shameful eviction and also of the desire to follow the example of their high-born tormentors. The Spanish notables had had their portraits painted by Velasquez and El Greco, the ejected ones got Rembrandt to paint theirs. True, they rarely came as patrons and customers, they only willingly complied with his wish that they should serve him as models.

It was thus that the portraits of Ephraim Bonus, the physician, of Menasseh ben Israel, the philosopher, and the several portraits of rabbis came into being and many hundred types from Rembrandt's neighbourhood fill his biblical etchings and paintings. There are women among them, they too, portraits captured on the Jodenbreestraat and the Houtgracht—as the Waterloo-Plein was called before the battle of Waterloo. Only the "Jewish bride", in the picture of that name, is no Jewish bride, but Rembrandt's own pure-blooded Aryan niece and the bridegroom by her side is no Jewish bridegroom, but the master's son Titus. But all the more authentically Jewish is, in the famous etching "Synagogue", the busy bustling of the tall-capped long-bearded figures in front of the temple steps. Rembrandt's Sephardic and Ashkenazi contemporaries live on in his paintings as King Saul and his harper David, also Jacob blessing his sons, as Haman and Esther, as blind Belisarius, as Abraham preparing to sacrifice his son.

In Rembrandt's orphaned dwelling the only book illustrations he ever made are kept in frames and under glass. They are illustrations for a poem in prose by his friend Menasseh ben Israel, entitled "Pedro Precioso". The hero indicated by the title is a stone: the stone on which Nebuchadnezzar stood, which is identical with the stone with which David slew Goliath, and with the stone on which

Daniel rested his head when he had his vision and also with the stone against which Jacob's ladder that led up to the sky was propped. On Nebuchadnezzar's body is a map showing four Persian provinces—this drawing was not made on Rembrandt's copperplate, but was added by Menasseh, the author and printer of "Pedro Precioso", for some crazy cabbalistic reason. Rembrandt thereupon, it is said, grew so angry that he broke off all relations with Menasseh.

For eighteen years Rembrandt lived in the street of the Jews. On the same day on which his creditors had an official inventory made of his house for the purpose of a forced auction, i.e. on 27th June, 1657, a Jewish inhabitant of the ghetto was also driven out of the community. But he was driven out by his own co-religionists.

Candles wrapped in black crêpe were placed in the chased silver sconces in which the Sabbath candles still mirror themselves with multicoloured reflections, and the same ram's horn which still announces the beginning and end of the great feasts droned the accompaniment to the judgment of exile pronounced by men who were themselves exiles: "May he be accursed at all hours of the day and may he be accursed at all hours of the night. May he be accursed when he lies down to his rest and accursed when he rises to his work. May he be accursed when he goes out and accursed when he returns home. The wrath and anger of the great God Zebaoth will flare up against him and the Lord Zebaoth will erase his name under the sky for ever and ever."

He who was thus anathematized was Baruch Spinoza; his name is not erased even if one cannot find his portrait in the mosaic of Mosaic figures which Rembrandt had picked out from his surroundings and immortalized for ever and ever. Rembrandt and Spinoza had friends in common. Spinoza's teacher was that Menasseh ben Israel whom Rembrandt had portrayed, and whose book he had illustrated. The patrons of both Rembrandt and Spinoza were the Huygens, father and son. It was Constantine Huygens who had discovered Rembrandt's genius in the cornloft of a mill on the Rhine and obtained for the miller's son commissions from Prince Maurits of Orange; the son of this Constantine Huygens, Christian Huygens, gave Spinoza work grinding lenses for the microscopes through which the research workers of the day began to study nature in order to find corroboration of their theories.

Rembrandt and Spinoza lived only a few paces from each other. Did the two ever meet? Nothing has come down to us on that point. It was not Rembrandt who immortalized Spinoza—much later it was Lessing, Goethe and Marx who proclaimed the glories of Spinoza's mind.

And those who ostracized him are as proud of him as they are of those who ostracized them. As proud as Spaniards, they marry only among themselves and squint down their noses at the *misera plebs*. They would never comply with the invitation extended to them by the Christ on the Antoniuskerk, but even less would they want to have anything in common with the Eastern Jews on the other side of Jonas-Daniel-Meijer Square.

Their ancestors were driven out by a jealous feudal aristocracy who hated them as representatives of the rising new power, that of mercantile capital, just as in another place the debt-ridden nobility of Poland directed the anger of the exploited common people against the noblemen's creditors. Southern Sephardim or Northern Ashkenazi, both are equally the victims of their own mercantilism, victims of jealous competitors. Nevertheless, the Spaniols do not conceal their upper-class contempt for the lower middle-class, even when the latter are their co-religionists, their fellow-sufferers, their companions in exile. To be refugees from the Spanish inquisition appears

to them as a fine thing, while the refugees from pogroms
seem to them to exhale a reek of poverty even after three
hundred years.

Although a great many of them have long been impoverished, although the community has long been split into
groups according to their wealth, they still all live in the
illusion that they are of "noble and wealthy lineage".
Diamond-cutters, even unemployed diamond-cutters, sit
under the temple chandeliers and are anxious to equal the
other "parnassimos senhores" and their own ancestors in
dignified bearing. Whoever were to tell them that they
are working men would insult them, and if anyone dared
to speak to them of working-class organization they would
draw their non-existing swords on him. They and the
unemployed clerks of the coffee and tobacco export busi-
nesses—or at least the older ones among them—prefer to
wait for a second Sabbathai Zevi to lead them by way of
the coffee and tobacco exchange, back to the golden days
of Aranjuez. No Sephardi Jew of Amsterdam, be he never
so poverty-stricken, would make an exhibition of himself
in the weekday market on the Waterloo-Plein, or in the
Sunday market on the Oude Schans, or, even worse, to cry
his name like an Ashkenazi, like the one who shouts all
day: "Heimann is *so* well known!"

CHAPTER SIXTEEN

Notes from the Paris Ghetto

Note 1. A genuine civil war is being fought out around the conception of *"kosher"* on the signs of the food shops in the Quartier St. Paul. Previously it had been thought that this word denotes conformity of certain foods to the ritual requirements; it was thought that what was not *kosher* was simply *trefa* and that the adjective *"kosher"* was not subject to comparison.

But now one finds that the term *"kosher"* is in much the same position as the term "national" is elsewhere. One party may be, well, national enough, the other party is more national of course, the third, it must be admitted, is more national still, but my own party is the most super-national of all and if you don't adhere to it, then you are a national traitor. There is a similar gradation in the ritual catering of Paris. Only one butcher's shop in the Rue des Ecouffes is content to display the three consonants of the word *"kosher"*. This plain statement is called in question by the next-door *boucherie, charcuterie et triperie*, it winks suggestively at the neighbouring shop and says of itself: *"emes kosher"*, I am *genuinely kosher*.

But what good does that do when a competitor on the other side of the street boasts of having as his customers the *"Shomrei Hadas"*, the Guardians of the Faith, so that even the most superlatively orthodox may buy their mutton and—the signs also announcing the sale of *"Ojfes-Volailles"*—their goose giblets, here in all confidence.

But one can make even surer than that: on the corner there is a butcher who, on the one hand describes himself as a *Maison de Confiance*, but on the other hand does not believe that his customers have *confiance* in him, for which reason he has put himself under the *"Haschgoche von bewussten Rav Harav Reb Joel Halevi Herzog, shilito"*.

Naturally these protestations of strict, stricter and strict-est ritual rectitude are displayed exclusively in Hebrew script, the French translation does not mention them at all and on one shop sign the announcement *"Adas Yisroel"* (most orthodox) on the left side, is flanked by a *"Boucherie Moderne"* in French.

As one says, this is all very double-tongued indeed. It is perhaps the Restaurant Haifa, in the Rue Vieille du Temple which deserves most confidence. For in the first place the bill of fare attached to the façade says: *"Kosher lemhadrin min lemhadrin"*, i.e. *kosher* for the strictest of the strict, and in the second place no translation tricks are practised here, as in the butcher's shop, which wants to be modern on the left and *Adas Yisroel* on the right. In the "Haifa" translations are literal. For instance there is a sign on the door: *"Fermez la porte, s.v.p."*, and as one does not expect the guests to know sufficient French, another sign beneath the first reads: *"Bitte zu fermachen der Tür beim Herausgehn."*

Note 2. Pain azyme is French for *matzos*. No *matzo* baker in Shepetovka or Berdichev ever suspected that his des-cendants would ply the same trade in Paris and that their bakery would be inscribed with the proud words: *"Fab-rique de Pain Azyme."* And when Moses, three and a half thousand years ago issued his strict commandment that in memory of the sufferings undergone during the wandering in the desert the Jews should eat unleavened bread for one week every year, he did not suspect either, what would come of this commandment. In the Paris ghetto, "Le Plätzl", one can buy *matzos* all the year round and the bread of austerity, the lenten food, has turned into a delicacy.

Note 3. Napoleonic proclamations, not slogans or the usual brief business advertisements, but truly napoleonic proclamations are the texts displayed on huge calico sheets above the little groceries:

"Our new mechanical matzo factory according the system of American matzo, what is baken clean, of best flour, strict kosher, the tastefullest matzos from all Paris. Demand everywhere, the Paris matzo, because it is guaranteed. Every matzo has the number 1934. We have received the golden medal in the exhibition, 1932. The matzo factory is under the *haschgoche* of Rav Joel Halevi Herzog."

Over the entrance to a house a banner is stretched with the legend:

"Here in the courtyard, has opened itself a new *épicerie*, the which it sells very very cheap. The best and freshest Shojre. Altogether the best fruits and the biggest eggs, just like in the *halles*. Also all the wines and pesach, goods under Horav Herzog. Everything sent to the house. You will save much money."

Even the street vendor issues manifestoes, especially if he happens to have changed his pitch:

"David Sonenbloum, what has been standing here in this entrance, has made himself a shop in the yard for *everything*, and is selling cheaper than anywhere else. Come in and convince yourself, you will be surprised, raisins, bananas, oranges, apples, barns, pommes de terre, tomates, cibelos, carottes, asperges."

Having enumerated every possible vegetable, he underlines in large letters, what else he stocks: "Légumes!"

Note 4. It was not when Louis XVI and his wife and children were escorted to Paris from Versailles by the women of the Halles, and the grandseigneurs and marchionesses fled to Coblenz, that the Jews settled in the vacated luxury quarters of Paris, the Quartier du Marais and the Quartier du Temple. In the winter of 1789 only the homeless Parisians of Christian faith, male and female, rag-tag-and-bobtail, moved into the deserted quarter. Thus it grew into a particularly ill-famed and hence particularly cheap region, and hence it could later serve as a suitable home for the miserable refugees from the pogroms in Russia and Poland.

Everything is still there: the palaces, the rag-tag-and-bobtail, and the Jews and none of the three factors has grown more handsome in the past 150 years. As for the palaces, one can only say: *sic transit gloria mundi.* For instance, No. 16 Rue Charlemagne was once the residence of Queen Bianca, mother of St. Louis; now it is Madame Korenbloum, *sage-femme*, who has got herself mixed up with the transition of *gloria mundi*, and the third floor is inhabited by David Chmoulkowicz, whose office it is to circumcise the boys brought into the world by the good offices of Mme Korenbloum.

On the site of No. 8 Rue Jardins St. Paul, once stood the house of a man whom, in his way, France honoured not less than St. Louis—the most unsaintly Rabelais. It was here, where to-day Jacques Axelchevaisse carries on his business as gut merchant, that Rabelais died, and from here he was taken to be buried in the Cimetière de St. Paul.

Other famous people were also buried in this cemetery; and also an unknown one, whose very anonymity made him a name in history: the Man in the Iron Mask. If, however, someone saw in this statement a reason for hoping that one might now exhume the body and thereby draw away the cast-iron veil covering the identity of that

N

prisoner in the Bastille, that someone would be disappointed, for all that is left of the Cimetière St. Paul is only the arch of one gateway—the graves are gone, there is no trace of the remains of Rabelais, of the Man in the Iron Mask and the other dead of their time. In the Passage St. Pierre, which leads from the Rue St. Paul to the Rue St. Antoine, and in which that cemetery arch stands, Maurice Finquellchtain now keeps a shop in which he sells coal and wine.

No. 38 Rue St. Paul was the prison of St. Eloi, the house next door, the administrative offices belonging to it and No. 12 in the Rue Charles V, was the house of that Balthazar Gobelin, whose son, Antoine, Marquis of Brunvilliers, married Marie d'Aubrai. After her marriage she had walked up and down the still well-preserved staircase before she became the most famous poisoner of all times. She may have dreamed as a child of her deadly future, but she certainly never dreamed that nuns and Jewish merchants would follow her as tenants of her hôtel. The congregation of pious sisters fits as ill into the house of the diabolical poisoner as into the neighbourhood of *matzo*-bakers and a candy factory. In the Rue Geoffroy d'Asnier, not far from the palace of the Cardinal Rohan, who allowed himself to be duped by Cagliostro, Anarchists argue every evening about individual revolution and stateless Communism. In the Hôtel Rohan itself, where the Cardinal received the jewellers who were to combine the most expensive pearls and diamonds in the world into a necklace for the Queen, Jewish outworkers sit and make up, with rubber solution, macintoshes, at four francs apiece, for the *Samaritaine* department store; it might be possible to make up ten of them in ten hours' work, if that much work could be had.

Note 5. The *genius loci*, a true-blue conservative genius, still hovers over this sometime aristocratic quarter. Although full-bottomed wigs and satin breeches are no longer to be found even in second-hand clothing shops, their contemporaries, the kaftan and temple-locks, can still be seen in its streets. The citizens of the Plätzl are full of patriarchal notions, a mixed marriage is as dishonourable to them as a *mesalliance* was to the original inhabitants of the quarter, and the synagogue in the Rue Pavée is as highly esteemed by them as was the church of St. Paul by the gentlemen of the League.

During the High Festivals the parish of St. Paul looks like the Eastern Jewish communities of Poland and Rumania, with the difference that in the east the number of synagogues and prayer-houses is stationary and adapted to the number of worshippers, while in the Plätzl, fluctuation upsets every possibility of calculation. Birobidzhan empties, Hitler fills. All dance halls are turned into temples for the Day of Atonement, in the whole district there is scarcely a house that has not been turned into a prayer-house from roof to basement. Rocking figures under silken beards and prayer-shawls fill the rooms and the galleries giving onto the courtyard so alarmingly that one fears the railings might break. In front of the house the children—boys in velvet suits, girls in light-coloured holiday best—wait until the unimportant parts of the divine service have been recited and Papa and Mama appear in the street.

Even "freethinkers" spend this sacred day in the synagogue. Crooked diamond-dealers from the Rue Lafayette, stock exchange brokers from the Rue du Quatre-Septembre, all sorts of touts who make their living by claiming to be able to obtain identity cards and working permits for stateless and paperless refugees—they all meet on this day to form a mass choir of coughing and the reeling-off of Hebrew words.

Chassidim, men of professional piety, are the leaders in the choir. The typical ghetto types, like Itzele Menagen and Ephraim Tzizik, who at other times hawk their topical Jewish songs from café to café, cough and pray with the others. Those who join in the coughing and praying include constituents of Socialist Léon Blum; include adherents of the militant Zionist Jabotinski; include neighbours of Schwarzbart, the man who shot Petljura, the Ukrainian bandit leader and Jew-slayer; include friends of the Anarchist Ataman Machno; include comrades of Menshevik leader Abramowitz; include old clo'es men from the Carreau du Temple; include the owners of the workshops in which best sandals are mended, knitted goods made, trousers tailored, leather coats stitched, macintoshes rubber-solutioned, ladies' coats pressed, underwear machined, caps sewn, or handbags provided with "pontschkes", (handles to you). Those who do not join in the coughing and praying and are not even present, are the workers in these small workshops and factories.

On the gallery reserved for the women, the fate of bas-de-chide Chane is the subject of lively discussion; this Hanna, only daughter of her parents, is being kidnapped every other day by white slavers in the serial novel appearing in the newspaper "Heint"; on the intermediate days Hanna is always rescued by her faithful lover. A stranger would scarcely understand the conversation. "*Meine Fiess gehn schon in die école*", does not mean that the lady's feet attend school, but that her son, *fils*, do so.

The seats in the temple for the High Festivals are not cheap; for a poor man such an expense means that he must fast another day after the great fast, and even the well-to-do do not like to spend so much money and then have nothing to show for it. But what can a man do? Once a year the sacrifice must be made, for the sake of the living children, in order that they may grow up to be pious and for the sake of the dead parents who had always been very pious, although their piety had not preserved them from the pogroms nor their posterity from the necessity of flight to the Paris "Plätzl".

Note 6. Restaurants keep their doors closed on the Day of the Fast and in the evening they have to face a multiplied assault of many hungry mouths. The cheap ones advertise "*Pri figs*" and "*Brojd a Dischkretion*"—the expensive ones have white tablecloths and many of their guests wear the red ribbon of the Legion of Honour in their buttonholes. "*Tous les jours spécialités des krépleches*", says the bill of fare, further, "*Poissons farcis*", "*Nüdelach avec Paveau*", "*Lokczen kes*", "*gefilté kiczke avec Farfel*" (note the *accent aigu* on the e in order that it may not be swallowed by the unenlightened) or "*Roti de veau avec kaché*". "*Scholet*" is written *scholet*, a conservatism which is out of place, for this word happens to be derived from the French, or so it is said: the "noble food of the Gods" was put into the warm bed (*chaud lit*) on Friday evening, in order to enjoy it warm on the Saturday without having to light a fire, this being banned by religious laws.

Fourneau alimentaire, the public soup-kitchen, is maintained by Rothschild. Rothschild is a famous name in Jewry, could there be a more famous one? There is one more famous, or at least one that was more famous at one time. It is the name of Captain Dreyfus. This same Captain Dreyfus is now inspector of the *école de travail* just opposite, a higher school for Jewish apprentices. "*Er kümmt presque jamais*", says the school caretaker, shrugging his shoulders, "but what would you, *aujourd'hui* he is a vieillard."

Note 7. In the gateways of the hôtels of the old nobility, junk dealers spread out their whole stock of dented cooking

pots, chipped cups, broken candlesticks and ragged clothing. The stone caryatids, witnesses of past glories, must
put up with slates on which, every day, the current price
of rags, waste paper, metal scrap and wood offcuts is
chalked up. In French this sort of trade is called *"brocante"*
a word that recalls brocade, but in Yiddish it is merely
"shmattes". In the baroque courtyard pieces of old linen
and other rags lie in heaps. The postern gate, once upon
a time used by the lackeys and on occasion by the marquise
herself slipping away to a secret love adventure, is now
the main entrance for the tenants of the house.

The *chiffonier*, the rag-merchant in the stricter sense of
the word, lives only by rags and waste paper. The window
of his tiny, mouldy shop is empty. After the beginning of
Hitler's rule of terror many such dealers covered the dim
glass of their shop doors with printed notices: *"Les représen-
tants des maisons allemandes ne sont pas reçus."* A grotesque picture this the representatives of German commercial houses,
stiff gentlemen in fur coats, a parcel of rags under the right
arm, a pile of old newspapers under the left arm, want to
pay a call on the *shmattes*-merchants in the narrow and
dirty Rue du Prévot, but then they catch sight of these
notices and withdraw in disappointment.

Ah, it is scarcely a matter for laughter. The poor rag-
dealer has taken the boycott propaganda seriously, with
which the "national" and religious Jews pretended to register
their protest against the persecution of their co-religionists
in Hitler Germany. In impotent fanaticism the rag-dealer
papered his tiny shop with the boycott notices and would
certainly refuse all trade with the enemy, were the deal
ever so profitable. His rich "comrades-in-arms" however,
waste not a thought on their promises if a profitable deal
is in view and the wholesaler who buys the little *chiffonnier's*
wares does business with Nazi Germany without any pangs
of conscience, whether he be Frenchman or Jew or both.

Thus the loudly proclaimed boycott has done nothing to stop the flood of horrors and infamies and the prayers in the Rue Pavée and the kosher, kosherer and kosherest meat, and the eating of *matzos* and the religious fast do not save the Jews in general from persecution, nor the poor *chiffonnier* in particular from his poverty.

But not only dealers and tradesmen live in the Plätzl there, as in Belleville and Montmartre, there are tens of thousands of other Jews, Jews who know that it is their class, not their race, against which the Fascist Reich has let loose torture and murder; who know that there can be no alliance between rich and poor and that a solidarity based on race and religion is Utopian. These other Jews know that they are the brothers of those German workers who are being put to death, imprisoned and tortured, and who work underground against the Nazis. These others put up no boycott stickers, these others fight resolutely against stupidity and reaction, for a world without ghettos and without classes.

CHAPTER SEVENTEEN

Indio Village Under the Star of David

I T was pitchdark night and pretty fresh at that as I got up this morning in order to arrive in Venta Prieta by seven o'clock.

I had heard rumours about this village and its Jewish inhabitants before, in Mexico City, but I did not know where it lay and I had even forgotten its name. But the day before yesterday I happened to travel to Pachuca, the silver city, and read, near kilometre stone 83 (counted from Mexico City) on a sign marking the entrance to a village, the name "Venta Prieta". Had that not been the name? I left the train and inquired uncertainly about the Jews. The man I had asked pointed with his finger: "That *caballista* over there is one of them."

A cabbalist? I could see no one anywhere near who might have been taken for an interpreter of numbers and portents, an adept of the Cabbala. There was only a peasant, just getting off his horse in quite unmystical fashion. Then I realized that a horse was "caballo" and so "caballista" must be a horseman. I approached the peasant and asked him: he replied that there was divine service every Saturday at seven in the morning.

Seven in the morning is not a pleasant hour. But what could I do? In the grey dawn, when all honest men are asleep, I jumped out of bed in Pachuca to go and meet the Sabbath. I must admit that I was expecting something grotesque and was in a somewhat ironical humour. An old music-hall turn came into my mind, that had been a hit in the days of harmless jargon fun. The Viennese music-hall comedian Eisenbach pranced about on the stage with a Red Indian feather head-dress on his head, Apache war paint all over him, but with Jewish side-curls and a prayer-shawl, such as Jews wear in the synagogue, and blared:

> Mein Vater war ein klaaner
> Jiddischer Indianer
> Mei Mutter tief im Texas drin
> War eine koschere Gänslerin . . . .

When I arrived in Venta Prieta it was too early as yet. A few Indios or *mestizos*, indistinguishable from other Indios or *mestizos*, stood about in the November fog, clad in linen shirts, trousers and sandals. One of them, stocky of build and wrapped in a red woollen shawl, was Senor Enrique Téllez, the head of the Jewish community. He was the man I had to see if I wanted authentic information. Senor Téllez is also the richest man in the village, although this does not in itself mean that he is a rich man.

Venta Prieta consists of one hundred and fifty people and a correspondingly small number of houses. Two-thirds of the inhabitants are Otomi Indios, though no longer pure-blooded. They work in the silver mines of Real del Monte, till the maize fields around the village, or breed *"havadas"*, guinea-fowl, a bird which like its breeders, is a product of miscegenation.

Only one side of the street is occupied by houses. They are slapped together out of adobe, street muck and horse manure. The only stone building is the school. On the other side of the road stretches an endless plain, with a military camp and an aerodrome for the secondary airline running to Guajutla in the Tampico region. A block of barracks gleams white in the distance.

"The third third," Senor Enrique Téllez tells me "are we Jews, thirty-seven adults. We are really only one large family, or more exactly two interrelated families, the Téllez and the Gonzalez."

"Have you been here long?"

"Only two generations. Before that we lived in Zamora, in the state of Michoacan. Forty years ago there was a pogrom outbreak there. The people seized my grand-father on the mother's side, Roman Gison was his name. They demanded that he embrace the Christian faith and scoff at his old faith. When he refused, they sewed him into a cow's hide and made a fire in a ring around it. The cowhide shrunk and pressed my grandfather to death. All the Jews fled from Zamora. My father found this farm here, which belonged to a distant hacienda. The soil is quite dry, all parched clods. But my father bought it because there were no other houses here—he did not want to live in a town any more, not even a village." Don Enrique pointed to a spot behind us: "That is where I was born."

"That" is a house, no less dilapidated and neglected than the others, but somewhat larger. All sorts of living things move in and out in lively traffic: guinea-fowl, chil-dren, a horse and many dogs. While Don Enrique is talking to me, a black cow sticks its head out of the gate, moos from time to time as though uttering a warning to beware of me and does not venture out of the yard, as though harbouring in her udders the deepest distrust of me.

I glanced at my watch. Don Enrique said: "The service will soon begin; we are not too punctual. The women must first make breakfast for their husbands who go out to work."

"Do they work on Saturday, then?"

"They have no alternative."

"Then how can they participate in the service?"

"We have three services, we come in three shifts."

"Do you yourself conduct the service, Senor Téllez?"

"No, I don't know much about it. Our rabbi is an Abyssinian."

"An Abyssinian? How did an Abyssinian get to Mexico?"

"He is working as a baker in Pachuca. He is a young man and very interested in religion. He knows the Bible well and can even read Hebrew. He'll be here in a minute."

Don Enrique enumerates the religious rites observed by the community. They fast on the Day of Atonement, "on the *Ayuno Mayor*", he translates, that I might understand. During the Passover they eat *matzoth*, "galletas de la semana santa", he translates, in words which I, for my part, would translate as "waffles of the holy week".

"We also observe New Year's Day and we fast on the anniversary of the destruction of the Temple. We eat no pork. We kill cattle and poultry *kosher* fashion."

I asked him whether they practised circumcision. "Yes, but we have no circumciser here. We take new-born boys to the city to Senor Klipper."

The Mexican circumciser does actually bear this ono-matopetic name.

Next to the black cow, who is still standing in the gate-way and watching me suspiciously, stands a little boy about four years old, a blonde Norwegian in appearance, who also stares at me with the same distrust.

"Come here," Don Enrique calls out to him, but in-stead of obeying, the little boy dashes away helter-skelter. "It's my nephew," says Uncle Henry. "I wanted him to tell you what his name is."

"What is his name?"

"Reuben. All our children are given Old Testament names. The boys are Elijah, Abraham, David, Saul; the girls Rachel, Rebecca or Sara. Do you know that Fran-cisco Madero's widow is also called Sara?"

I had already heard in Mexico City that the martyrs of national freedom, the brothers Francisco J. Madero and Gustavo Madero had been secret Jews and so was Francisco Madero's widow, who was now living in New York; her maiden name was Pérez, a typical Spaniol Jewish name. The Madero brothers are not the only great Mexicans who are rumoured to be of Jewish origin. The inquisition had described many of its victims as "judaizante" "leaning towards Jewry", with the purpose of defaming them. The father of the Mexican nation, Father Miguel Hidalgo, himself is booked in the documents of the Inquisition relating to him, as "judaizante".

"Our children," the head of the community continues, "attend the general school. Have you seen the school-house? Fine, isn't it? A few years ago the Cristeros (a clerico-fascist movement) declared that Venta Prieta must have a church. Thereupon the inhabitants of the village—they are mostly miners and all of them are organized in the trade unions, so they are not anti-Semites—appealed to to the government and asked for a school instead, as there was already one church in the village. That this church was a Jewish temple, they did not say. We got the school, it was inaugurated when Ortiz Rubio was President. One of our boys, Saul Gonzalez, attends the school over there in the military camp, and one of our men works on the aerodrome, he first helped out a bit as a mechanic and later passed his test for a pilot."

Don Enrique's knowledge of the history of the Jews in Mexico is limited to acquaintance with the name of Carbajal, the Portuguese whom Philip II sent to New Spain in order to pacify the insurgent coastal regions. Luis Carbajal, the Elder, brought a hundred marrano families with him and it is from these that the Mexican Jews claim to have descended. But they honour above all the elder Carbajal's nephew, "Carbajal el Mozo", who was tortured in the dungeons of the Inquisition together with his mother and sisters, but refused to deny his Jewish faith. On 5th December, 1596, he and his whole family, forty-five Jews in all, were burned at the stake; this number does not include the dead whose remains were dug up from the graveyards, nor those who fled and could be burned only *in effigie*. There was also a German with them; as an inconvertible Lutheran he had been imprisoned in the dungeons of the Inquisition and there had been converted by Carbajal—to the Jewish faith. Luis Carbajal el Mozo and his family were burned as impenitent Jews.

Of his own generation, Don Enrique has a little more to say:

"In Michoacán we had a Rabbi who was not beardless like the Indios but had a great silver beard; the peasants called him "the bishop of the Jews". Sometimes he journeyed to other Jewish communities to preach to them. In our district there is no Jewish community beside our own. The nearest is two hours' rail journey from here, in San Agustin de Zapoctla, a village in the state of Mexico. Ah, here comes our Rabbi. Olé, Etiope!"

The Ethiopian, thus accosted, approaches us. In his hand he carries a parcel carefully tied up with string. Because I know that he is an Abyssinian, I immediately find him to be a typical Falasha from Abyssinia. In the Judeo-Christianity of the Falashas the Jewish tendency seems to preponderate, for Falashas abroad are mostly Jews—I saw their great synagogue in the Harlem district of New York and now here I find a rabbi of their tribe.

His name is Guillermo Pena, he is scarcely thirty years old and understands only a few words of Kuara, the language of the Falashas. Guillermo Pena lives in Pachuca with his father and there bakes just so much bread as he himself can deliver on his rounds, that is, not much. Thus he has the leisure to teach himself Hebrew and to read the Bible. Every Saturday morning he comes to Venta Prieta, holds divine service and gives religious instruction without any remuneration at all. This Rabbi is a shy and some-what embarrassed young man, who does not like to answer my questions and is glad when I comply with his invitation to come into the "Jardincito".

The "Jardincito" is the little garden surrounded by a red brick enclosure and the name includes the prayer-house that is in the garden. It might hold forty people at the utmost. A spirit lamp dangles from the ceiling. A rickety upright piano stands in one corner, in the other is a black-board covered with Hebrew script characters in chalk, and as a second educational accessory, a battered globe used to visualize biblical geography. Three vases made of bits of mirror, with paper flowers in them, are intended to beautify the upright piano.

On the embroidered cover of the altar table there is a candle (instead of the seven-armed candelabrum), a glass (instead of the golden chalice) and, instead of a hand-written parchment *Torah* scroll, there is a large book: the Old and New Testaments in Spanish, published by the Bible Society. Truly this book is out of place here from every point of view: neither does the Jewish community recognize the New Testament, nor did the Bible Society publish the book in order that it may assist the Jews in maintaining their Jewish faith.

Whitewashed walls. One of the walls bears a painted Star of David held by two lions with bare bodies but bushy manes around their heads. To make up for the lack of real candelabra, two are painted on another wall, but— might as well go the whole hog—their bases and the candles in them are decorated with all sorts of emblems. The frontal wall is dominated by the "Hear, Israel" prayer in Hebrew and Spanish: "Oye, Israel, el eterno es nuestro dios, el eterno uno es."

Don Guillermo has anxiously watched my contempla-tion of these frescoes and when I asked who had painted them he answered with a timid: "I did," adding as an afterthought, "I am a baker, senor,"

"The pictures are very fine, especially the Hebrew writing," I nodded amiably and saw a blush spread over the African dark-brown of his face. "I am a baker, senor," he whispers a second time.

Don Guillermo is, perhaps, no painter, but he is more than just a baker. In the first place he is a priest, as one can see when he tenderly undoes his little bundle and spreads out its contents, which is music and prayer books with many markers in them. Then a white shawl comes out of a little bag and the rabbi puts it round his neck, and also a little skullcap which is fitted tightly on the back of his head.

The congregation consists of thirteen persons of the Jewish faith, i.e. three more than the prescribed minimum. But for all that the thirteen do not constitute a quorum, because women and children do not count. But can Jehovah be so strict about such a thing here, where His people remained steadfastly faithful to him despite centuries of terrible threats and alluring promises?

During those centuries the word was passed from hut to hut: "Let us pray!" with the time and place given in a whisper. Only in the jungle was there space for a divine service. On the way there one could be pierced by Indian arrows or seized by the familiars of the Inquisition, one could fall into a crater or be torn to pieces by wild beasts. If then one of the *minjen* did not arrive, perhaps precisely the tenth man, should then the other nine go home again with nothing to show for their pains? "Never mind, let us pray," they said, and prayed. And because Jehovah condoned this at the time, in Mexico now a *minjen* is a *minjen* even if less than ten men are gathered together.

To-day the number of men is four. There are also four women or girls. It is they who have embroidered flowers and biblical sayings on the altar-cloth and who now break into the monotonously muttered prayer-texts with their song. The children join in the singing, among them the Norwegian-Jewish-Indian Reuben Téllez, who ran away from me a minute ago, and also the nine-year-old Saul González, who attends the military school and is a future Mexican general.

The divine service was simple, but at bottom a Sabbath service like other Sabbath services elsewhere. At the end the congregation stood up in front of the altar to speak the prayer for the dead. Children may not say this prayer until they have been admitted by confirmation to the religious community. But here two boys, probably orphans, stepped forward together with the adults—another of the exceptions granted by God to the village of Venta Prieta in Mexico.

I, too, stepped forward, stood up with my feet close together and repeated after the Rabbi what the Rabbi said —only the names of his own dead did each worshipper insert for himself.

My father and my mother were born in Prague, lived there, died there and are buried there. Never could they have imagined that a son of theirs would speak the prayer for the dead for them with a group of Indios, in the shadow of the silver-lined mountains of Pachuca. My parents, who had spent their lives in Bear House in the old town of Prague, did not suspect that their sons would one day be driven from Bear House, one to Mexico, to India another, and the two who were unable to escape the Nazi terror, to unknown places of unimaginable horror and to death. My thoughts ranged further: relatives, friends, acquaintances and strangers, victims of Nazi terror, they all could claim to be remembered in the prayer for the dead.

A procession of millions, men and women who had spent their lives in the striving to provide for their families and

bring up their children to be useful members of human
society; workers who earned their bread in the sweat of their
brow; physicians, prepared day and night to go to the assis-
tance of those who suffered; men who did their best to spread
the truth and improve the lot of their fellow-men; scholars
who lived for the advancement of science; artists who strove
to bring beauty into our lives; children who dreamed of a
wonderful future for themselves . . . all sorts of people,
jolly and sentimental, good and bad, weak and strong.

They come, countless, in an interminable procession.
Past cold and brutal faces they stagger towards the goal.
There it is, a building from which smoke rises. They all
know what that building is, and what the smoke is made
of that rises from the chimney. It is a death factory, it
manufactures corpses. What were the thoughts of this
army of victims-for-the-slaughter as they moved towards
this goal? There was no more hope, no hope for themselves, for their children, for their memory, scarcely hope
even of retaliation, of punishment for this mass murder.
They must press through the gates, they must strip, they
must go into the chamber where a terrible gas suffocates
them, burns them, dissolves them into nothing. Smoke
rises from the chimney.

Interminable is the procession, it moves along as though
there had never been a humanity, as though there had
never been any meaning to humanity, never the striving
to bring more bread, more justice, more truth, more
health, more wisdom, more beauty, more love and more
happiness into this world.

I am the last to leave the altar, towards which I had set
out a few hours before in such merry humour.

CHAPTER EIGHTEEN

The Murderers Built a Mausoleum for their Victims

I

T H I S was the plan: to exterminate a nation of many millions and then to demonstrate by means of a museum which was to be established by the murderers, what fanatical and dangerous enemies of the millennial Third Reich the victims, i.e. the Jews, had been. The richer and bigger we make this museum—such was the argument of the Nazis—the more convincingly it will show the coming generations how fundamentally we have changed the world, how greatly we influenced the course of history. "But I,"—the executor of the plan, the Obersturmbannführer added in his thoughts—"I will get a lecturership out of it."

It didn't come off as planned. And it may yet come to pass that the fugitive Obersturmbannführer and former future lecturer will turn up one day to claim a reward from the Jews for his creation of the mausoleum-museum. Of course it wasn't so completely his creation: the foundation for it was the historical collection of the Israelitic community of Prague. But the Nazis provided plenty of additions. Day after day the synagogues were stormed and looted and for the equipping of the museum there was more manpower available than ever Pharaoh had for the building of the pyramids. The slaves of the Nazis did not even need to be given the amount of consideration required to keep them alive for further toil. On the contrary, their death was part of the whole project.

But not only this exploitation of man-power, an exploitation that transcended even death, was unprecedented. The suitability of these slaves for the purpose was also without precedent. For they belonged to the race which was to be destroyed and knew the material better than any ethnographer ever knew the material of his field of research. There was scarcely an unskilled labourer among them who did not try to transform this enterprise of hate into a labour of love, who did not try to permeate it with his own faith. And they succeeded!

How could they succeed? How could it come to pass that these who had commissioned the work had allowed themselves to be cheated of their purpose?

The handful of Jews who have survived their collaboration in the establishment of the museum, insist on believing in a miracle. They think that although in the beginning it had been the ambition of the Obersturmbannführer to achieve a university lecturership which had prompted him to include only impeccably authenticated objects, at a later stage the evidence provided by these objects had finally succeeded in convincing and converting him and his staff.

No, no, the founders of this museum had never, either voluntarily or involuntarily intended to exhibit proofs controverting their beliefs. They believed in the thousand-year duration of their Reich and accordingly planned for long-term operations. The part of the work for which they had exploited the productive knowledge of their slaves, was intended to serve merely as a pedestal for a monstrous monument of defamation, but on the apex up above there was to be an apotheosis of the Blonde Warrior hurling World Jewry for ever into the abyss.

"Tobias," the Obersturmbannführer used to say pleasantly to his expert assistant, Dr. Jakubowitz, "Tobias, you will be the last Jew whose scalp I will collect."

One day he collected the scalp by sending Dr. Tobias Jakubowitz to the gas chamber. It was the day on which the Obersturmbannführer saw the pedestal completed.

For the rest of the monument, the upper part, he no longer needed any Jews.

But precisely this moment brought the sudden change in which the faithful saw the hand of God and which scientific Socialists call the dialectical turn. The Red Army, said to have long since been scattered to atoms, marched into Prague and the Nazis fled as though the demon of their own invention was on their heels . . . .

II

The museum has two sections. One of them, "The Ghetto of Prague", was found shelter in the building of the Burial Brotherhood within the enclosure of the ancient Jewish cemetery, subject of so many legends. The cemetery like the old synagogue, dating back to the early Middle Ages, was left standing as an extramural extension of the museum, and closed down. It was to have been reopened only when there were no more living Jews left to come and visit the dead.

Before dealing with this section we must make this editorial apology: we have only a native of Prague as our reporter, i.e. not one who might be surprised by the various exhibits. For him most of these things are memories, familiar things seen again.

For instance here is the ragged, frayed five-pointed standard of originally light-brown brocade, long familiar to our reporter. In his infancy it was proof of the existence of a world of adventure. On certain feast-days the standard and a no less ancient shirt were brought out of the temple safe-deposit and an official, surrounded by the faithful in general and boys in particular, would explain its significance: this banner and this shirt had belonged to a certain Molcho who, together with his friend Reubeni, had led a Jewish revolution in Italy, had wanted to proclaim a kingdom of the Jews and had perished heroically at the stake.

In stark contrast to Molcho's shirt hangs Mordecai Meisl's temple curtain, a glory of spun gold and coloured embroidery. It roused the shy admiration of the adults perhaps even more than the relics of the heroic Molcho stirred the imagination of the youngsters. For Mordecai Meisl, who had given employment to the whole guild of Jewish embroiderers-in-gold with the making of this curtain, had been so rich that the German Emperor Rudolf II had constantly borrowed money from him. After Rudolf's death a law-suit was initiated about the borrowed money, in which the Tyrolese peasant boy played the part of Shylock and the Jewish creditors were the persecuted ones.

No less rich than the donor of the rich temple curtain was the donor of the rich *torah* cover that hangs next to it. This was Pinchas Oppenheim, who employed an orangutan ape as watch dog for his house. No watch of armed soldiers, no pack of fierce dogs would have inspired unauthorized visitors with greater fear than the ape. And when it died it continued to stand on guard: Pinchas Oppenheim had him stuffed and stood up at the window out of which he stared with bared teeth. But one day the orang-utan tumbled over and vomited coined gold. Whether it had swallowed the ducats one by one in the course of time, or whether Pinchas Oppenheim had used it as a safe after its death is a point on which the legends of Prague, the *Sippurim* (tales) are not unanimous.

Many documents of the museum remind our reporter of his friend, Siegmund Reach. All his life Siegmund Reach was a poor and unassuming bookseller in the Schalengasse and remained all his life a poor and unassuming bookseller in the Schalengasse for the sole reason that he wasted all his time and money on his mistress of the hundred-pointed crown, the city of

Prague. He nosed out everything in Prague and any-where else in the world that had any reference to Prague, had it photographed and reproduced. He also recorded all landmarks that were sacrificed to the needs of new building. Nothing of his beloved should be lost without a trace if he could help it. And hence he, too, shall not be lost without a trace, he who found an atrocious death at the hand of the Nazis together with his whole family. Siegmund Reach had helped many authors with his suggestions and one of these, a man named Strobel, said as much in the preface to his book *The Torch of the Master*. But when the brown brutes came to power, Herr Strobel hurriedly withdrew the preface and in a new preface whined for mercy for having written the first one a year before. It is a pity that the museum displays no portrait of Siegmund Reach, the poor and unassuming bookseller of the Schalengasse, for there should be honour where honour is due. As an illustration, the two prefaces of the Nazi author should also be exhibited, for there should be infamy where infamy is due.

III

This shoe here belonged until the most recent time to the rabbinate court in Prague and was ever ready for use. But our reporter, who is a native of Prague, first heard of this shoe and its purpose in Tunis and described it as a curiosity. The purpose of the shoe is this: if a man dies without issue, his brother, unless deaf-mute, married or renegade, is under the obligation of taking the widow for his wife and continue his brother's line. Should he have no inclination to do this, the widow is expected to confront her discourteous brother-in-law in the presence of the elders in the community and return his insult in kind. She must pull his shoe off his foot, spit out in front of the boorish one and slap his face, saying as she does so: "May every man fare thus who refuses to build his brother's house! Amen!"

In the Rabbinical Court of the rabbinate one could also get rid of one's partner in marriage. Letters of divorce issued in Prague and dating back to the early Middle Ages or modern times hang on the walls of the museum; they are chiefly remarkable because they are not dated Prague, for cities are not built for eternity and may change their names. Rivers and lakes change their names far less frequently. For this reason the Prague divorce decrees were dated from the locality "demiskarja Mezigrady (Wyschegrad-Hradschin), dejoswo al nehar M Wiltawa weal nahar Butiz" a phrase which can be translated only by one with an equal command of Aramaic and the Prague local idiom. "The stream Butiz" probably never more than a rivulet, has been bricked over and lost even the last remnants of its sight and smell. But the Wiltawa (Vltava) is still called by that name although for three hundred years the official Austrian language and after that the Nazis permitted no other name but "Moldau". The castles Wyschehrad and Hradschin also still exist, just like the city area of Prague that lies between the two, together with the Jewish community.

IV

Strange things pertained to this community. Such was for instance the Golem, the homunculus kneaded out of clay (and known as "homunkeles" in Prague). His memory is kept green in the museum by a late drawing of the Czech artist Mikulas Ales, showing a Golem with Jewish features. In their anti-Semitic propaganda throughout the "Protectorate of Bohemia and Moravia" the Nazis turned the Golem into a symbol of Christians controlled and exploited by the Jews.

That the great Rabbi Löw created the Golem is a myth; but he really did create the rules of the burial brotherhood of Prague, whose seat now houses the museum. Ever since the Thirty Years' War the brotherhood has held a celebration of thanksgiving on the eve of Rosh-chodesh-Shevat at the graveside of the man who gave them their laws. From the window of their house one can see that grave, and by looking at one of the sixteen paintings hung up on the walls of this house two centuries ago, one can see how this celebration was held then, just as it is still held to-day. The grave and the pictures have outlived all deaths here, even the death of Nazism.

V

In contrast to the Prague section, in which our reporter felt at home, in the neighbouring Klaus synagogue, which houses the section "World Jewry", he felt almost like a visitor from the purely Aryan future of which the Nazis dreamed. And yet these exhibits by no means come from distant places. They were brought here from synagogues in Moravia, Silesia and Slovakia and from the dwellings of their worshippers. What the brown burglars, incendiaries and murderers found there and did not think valuable enough to put into their own pockets, was sent to the Nazi "Institute for Research into the Jewish Question" for inclusion in the Prague museum, and thus these relics of the historic cultural monuments destroyed by the Vandals have been preserved.

Just beyond the entrance an arm stretches out towards those who enter, as though to seize them by the throat. But all it wants is to touch their hearts: it is of brass and in its palm is a slit intended to take the coin of offering. Thus insistently and menacingly---never has our reporter seen anything even remotely as direct on bell-bag or poor-box—are alms collected in the synagogues and cemeteries of this demi-Asia.

The ritual demands that on the doorpost of every Jewish house a little tube be fastened on a slant. It looks like a clinical thermometer but contains no temperature scale but a blessing written on parchment as protection against all harm. For the entrance to a museum a single *Mezuzah* is of course insufficient. An endless number of them is nailed up here and they come bigger and bigger the more easterly their place of origin. Great as the fear of the Jews may have been of betraying to the pogrom-makers that their house was a Jewish one, their faith that the *Mezuzah* had the power to ward off pogroms was obviously even greater.

Much that is in the glass cases and on the walls is known in Western Europe only from hearsay, if at all. Here is a representation of "*kapporos*", the substitute sacrifice of a hen. He who offers the sacrifice swings a hen in a circle over his own head, thereby transferring his own destiny to the hen. Or here are the rods used by pious men to scourge themselves with thirty-nine strokes on the eve of the Day of Atonement.

VI

Each glass case is dedicated to a different aspect of the Jewish faith, illustrated by a copper engraving dating from the eighteenth century. At that time several books were published in Germany, mainly for the purpose of converting and persecuting the Jews; the most fatal of these were the *Hand Mirror* by Pfefferkorn, himself a proselyte; J. A. Eisenmann's *Jewry New Discovered*; and Wagenseil's *Tela Ignea Satanae*—anti-Semitic books of hatred, full of distorted quotations twisted from their meaning and specially suitable for fresh use by "Stuermer" and Streicher.

But the Jewish slave-labourers forced to work on the museum gave little information to the organizer of the enterprise regarding the books written by his predecessors. They mentioned only one book, the work of Christian G. Bodenschatz, published in four volumes in Erlangen in the year 1784 under the title: *Ecclesiastical Constitution of the German Jews in our day.* It is from this book, an objective, perhaps even pro-Jewish one, that the texts and copper-plate engravings were taken; they illustrate, in fivefold photographic enlargement, the exhibited objects.

The Nazis thought that visual education, a wax-work-like presentation of Jewish scenes would be more popular and also make a deeper impression on the spectator. Here the fanatical initiators of the scheme might have given full vent to their spite in exaggeration, untruth and caricature, had not the resistance of their helpers been once more successful.

In a room furnished in early nineteenth-century style, life-size wax effigies sit at their Passover meal, leaning back in their chairs as prescribed for that evening. The grandfather wears the white gown that is soon to be his shroud; the master of the house is arranging a selection of herbs and unleavened bread; the mistress of the house, a richly decorated bonnet on her head, is concerned with the food and the son is looking at the book with many pictures with the aid of which he is about to ask the questions relating to the significance of the feast. An empty chair and a goblet on the table in front of it are reserved for *Elianove*, the prophet Elijah, who partakes of the meal in such strict incognito that he remains invisible. In the wall gapes an artificial bit of wreckage, the "*Churban Beth Hamikdash*" which means: never forget the destruction of the Temple in Jerusalem.

When the figures were shown to him, the Obersturm-bannführer shouted, highly incensed: "I don't like those noses, they must be made longer by an inch, no, an inch and a half!"

So the waxwork sculptor lengthened the noses by the prescribed number of inches, but the feasting family lost not an inch of their dignity for all that.

According to the story told by those who witnessed the birth of the museum, the Obersturmbannführer was also extremely angry when he saw the model of ritual slaughter. "Is this supposed to be cruelty to animals? I'll show you what cruelty to animals looks like!" He ordered the cow about to be slaughtered to be given a suffering and reproachful expression, a horrible pool of blood to be added and the slaughterman to wear a sadistic, revolting grin.

He had also intended to make his Jews produce a plastic representation of a ritual murder, but he reluctantly gave up this plan after the former experiences, although only for the time being. The job was to be entrusted later to the sculptors of the dawning era in which no Jews would be in existence any longer; they might then use the pictures in the Stürmer as their models. But this project could not be carried out either.

VII

The criminal origin of the museum is indicated above all by the fact that the exhibits include a large number of specimens that differ only very slightly from each other. Had the collection been assembled little by little and completed according to requirements by purchase or barter instead of by mass looting, there would of course be no such plurality. "We suffer from *embarras de richus*" said our learned cicerone Dr. Muneles, punning on the French word *richesse* and the Hebrew word *rishus* which means anti-Semitism.

The ritual drapes, two thousand five hundred of them, had to be stored in special depots, for the walls of the museum offered far too little space for the display of these hangings. They are of heavy brocade made even heavier by chased and spun gold. They would, of course, be even heavier than they are had not every one of the "collectors" broken out a few pearls and precious stones in order to drape his own pockets with them.

On the lid of a renaissance goblet—it is said to have belonged to the great Rabbi Löw—a youthful David, an embarrassed smile on his face, sets his foot on the severed head of Goliath. The nowhere visible and yet omnipresent prophet Elijah is offered his draught in goblets, on the reliefs of which one may see him being wafted to heaven while alive—the only ascension of a living being. *Kiddush* goblets are here, made of ruby-red Bohemian glass and inscribed with Hebrew letters. A profane tumbler bears the word *lechayim*, "your good health". The great jug of the burial brotherhood shows a funeral procession, not painted or in relief, but consisting of cast figures, like lead soldiers.

Thus the people which was forbidden to make itself images of what was in the heavens above or the earth here below, did not entirely renounce at least the lower part. But mostly it gave vent to its passion for sculpture in ornamental designs.

Even the *shofar*, the ramshorn which emits such shrill tones at certain points in the divine service, is engraved with ornaments; nor are they missing from the tomahawk with which the *shoolklopfer* knocks on the doors of sluggard members of the congregation in order to wake them in time for the service. Synagogue pillars and household utensils, circumcision knives and tombstones, collecting boxes and devotional accessories show curious meanders, among them many containing elements both of *magen David* and swastika.

Wonderful are the "*B'somim*", the massive or filigree little boxes for balsam, incense and rose-water which lie on a dish beside a plaited candle. All this is needed for Princess Sabbath when she visits a poor Jew on Friday evening to spend a happy night and a happy day with him and then, when the week-end is drawing to a close, to offer him her golden box of nard.

> "Slowly sniffs he, to enjoy it;
> Then the Princess doth present him
> With a stirrup-cup; he drinketh
> Hastily and in the goblet
> Leaveth but a drop or two.
> These he sprinkles on the table
> Takes a little waxen taper
> Dips it in the moisture till it
> Crackles, hisses and is quenched."

But there is no need for Heine's poetic eye in order to see the lady: every Friday evening, at the last verse of the Sabbath hymn all worshippers in the Old-new-synagogue of Prague turn their backs towards the holy east, face the door and take one step towards the entering Princess. How lovely she is! Her picture is mirrored in every eye and if there was any man there who doubted the reality of the visitor, he could see her in the eyes of the other worshippers.

But we are not at divine service in the Old-new-synagogue. This is an ordinary working day and we are in a museum. In front of us the helmet of a Prussian grenadier is standing to attention; after its discharge from military service it has been transformed into a seven-branch candlestick. Gad, Sir, it never expected such a luminous resurrection when it flew off the head of its wearer or together with the head of its wearer on a Bohemian battlefield.

The frames in the museum are a story in themselves, a framework, so to speak. A *Mizrach* clamped in corrugated silver indicates the direction from which help will come when Hitler is greatest. Not far from it is a timetable with several dials but they do not show the departure of trains to the Promised Land but the hours of divine service. In a glittering frame a *Shivisi* flaunts itself although by rights it should be hiding itself modestly. At one time it used energetically to impress on the Jewish players and minstrels—who, in addition to these pursuits, also acted as singers in the temple—that they were not to mistake the altar for a stage. They were to remember the framed words: "*Shivisi*—I let the word of God be before my eyes."

Standing in front of this warning sign, we are already quite close to the literary work attributed to God. The Jew who is called up in the temple, first sanctifies himself by giving thanks to the divine Author and only after that does he do his office. With suitable ceremony he first strips the hand-written book of its splendid wrappings, the breastplate with the symbols of the twelve tribes, the regal crown, the two sceptres and orbs with their tinkling bells. Then he raises the Book—which is now only a parchment scroll—for all the congregation to see and even the most suspicious among the worshippers must admit: "Yes, this is it, this is the Law."

But . . . could not the man who is to read aloud a section of the Book of the Law—can he not falsify, can he not omit something? No, that he cannot! For beside the reader stands an overseer well versed in the Bible, with a silver slate-pencil in his hand and runs it along the sacred lines both supervising strictly and assisting helpfully.

He who reads aloud pays attention only to the letters, and the wise one who points at the wisdom of the scroll with his pointer pays attention only to the lines.

But in the museum it is the silver slate-pencil that gets attention. There are many of these in the museum. All are in the shape of a hand with outstretched index finger, and they are all delicate and all ornamented, each in its own way. Tiny fingers wear tiny rings of various periods and even the nails appear manicured according to varying fashions and national customs. And none of the hands is merely a hand—they are always parts of an arm, sometimes a bare arm with muscles, wrists and elbows, sometimes a clothed arm with a fine laced cuff and embroidered sleeve of dully gleaming metal.

The raised part of the hall, designated with the Arab word "al memor" was the sanctuary of the Bible. Here stood the Book, teacher and judge at once, recognized as infallible and incontestable not only by its own people, but by Christians and Moslems, heretics and sectarians, and philosophers of all varieties including atheists.

Up there, lying in state like a corpse, it was to show the coming generations of the thousand-year-old Nazi Reich what an overwhelming position the brown storm-troops had taken by assault when they overthrew the old teachings of the Bible for ever and set up in its place for all time the saving doctrine of Hitler.

But the Bible remains in its place while Hitler's Reich burst like a bubble with an evil smell nine hundred and ninety years before the fullness of the thousand years.